RUSSIA'S LOMONOSOV

RUSSIA'S

CHEMIST · COURTIER

PHYSICIST · POET

LOMONOSOV

BY BORIS N. MENSHUTKIN

PRINCETON, NEW JERSEY : 1952

PRINCETON UNIVERSITY PRESS

PUBLISHED FOR THE RUSSIAN TRANSLATION PROJECT
OF THE AMERICAN COUNCIL OF LEARNED SOCIETIES

TRANSLATED FROM THE RUSSIAN BY JEANNETTE EYRE
THAL AND EDWARD J. WEBSTER UNDER THE DIRECTION
OF W. CHAPIN HUNTINGTON

Printed in the United States of America
By Princeton University Press, Princeton, N.J.

FOREWORD

MENSHUTKIN AND HIS STUDIES ON LOMONOSOV[1]

BY TENNEY L. DAVIS

Boris N. Menshutkin's biography of Lomonosov, translated here into English for the first time, is the best qualified of any to make this extraordinary man known to English readers. It is the fruit of a lifetime of study by the man who first called attention effectively to the scientific writings of Lomonosov, who edited them from manuscripts in the archives of the Russian Academy of Sciences, and who by many publications has made Lomonosov known to the scientific world. It has long been well known that Lomonosov occupies an important place in the history of Russian language and culture, but the facts concerning his contributions to science, particularly to chemistry, are only gradually, and not yet sufficiently, finding their way to the knowledge of students. It is due to the efforts of Menshutkin that college students of chemistry hear the name of Lomonosov, but even now the name does not always appear in the newest books on the history of chemistry.

Menshutkin's first publication on Lomonosov was a book in Russian, *M. V. Lomonosov Considered as a Physical Chemist*, published in 1904. This was followed in the next year by an article in German, "M. W. Lomonossow, der erste russische Chemiker und Physiker," published in *Annalen der Naturphilosophie*, and in 1909 by a chapter on "M. W. Lomonossows Satz der Erhaltung der Energie und des Stoffes," in the Georg W. A. Kahlbaum Festschrift volume entitled *Beiträge aus der Geschichte der Chemie*. In

---

[1] Rewritten in large part from the article, "Boris N. Menshutkin's Contributions to the History of Chemistry," *Journal of Chemical Education*, 15, 203-209 (1938).

1910 No. 178 of Ostwald's *Klassiker der exakten Wissenschaften* appeared, "Physikalisch-chemische abhandlugen M. W. Lomonossows, 1741-1752," consisting of excerpts from Lomonosov's writings translated into German from Russian and Latin and edited by B. N. Menshutkin and Max Speter, and accompanied by Menshutkin's notes. Through this book Alexander Smith became interested in Lomonosov, and his presidential address delivered before the American Chemical Society at Washington, December 28, 1911, was based upon it and upon Menshutkin's earlier publications in German. This address, "An Early Physical Chemist, M. W. Lomonosov," was printed in the *Journal of the American Chemical Society*, 34, 109-119 (February 1912)[2] at the same time that a somewhat fuller article in English by Menshutkin, "Bicentenary Anniversary of M. V. Lomonosov's Birthday," appeared in the *Chemical News*, February 16 and 23, 1912. For fifteen years these two articles constituted the only sources in the English language of information about Lomonosov. Stillman in his *The Story of Early Chemistry*[3] cited Alexander Smith's article and Ostwald's *Klassiker* No. 178, but overlooked Menshutkin's English paper.[4] Since 1912 the only authoritative new publication in English on Lomonosov has been an article by

[2] It has been reprinted (with portrait) in L. A. Goldblatt's book, *Collateral Readings in Inorganic Chemistry* (New York and London, 1937), pp. 17-22.

[3] J. M. Stillman, *The Story of Early Chemistry* (New York and London, 1924), pp. 511-513.

[4] Except for No. 178 of Ostwald's *Klassiker der exakten Wissenschaften*, the only non-Russian *book* on Lomonosov with which we are acquainted, previous to now, is the interesting and attractive volume by the Marquis de Lur-Saluces, *Lomonossof, le Prodigieux Moujik* (Paris 1933), which contains a general survey of his life and character and of his work as linguist, prosodist, lyric poet, dramatist, historian, geographer, astronomer, physicist, chemist, statesman, educator, and maker of mosaics. The author cites Menshutkin's 1911 biography of Lomonosov as well as several earlier biographies in the Russian language.

Menshutkin, "A Russian Physical Chemist of the Eight-eenth Century," published with portrait in the *Journal of Chemical Education*, 4, 1079-1087 (September 1927).

Boris Nikolayevich Menshutkin was born on April 29, 1874, the son of Nikolay Aleksandrovich Menshutkin, who was professor of chemistry in the University of St. Peters-burg from 1865 to 1902 and in the Polytechnic Institute up to the time of his death, January 23, 1907 (O.S.), three days after the death of Mendeleyev. B. N. Menshutkin completed his studies at the university in 1895, and after that time taught chemistry, first at the university as assistant to his father (seven years, up to 1902), then as chief assist-ant in the Polytechnic Institute. In 1907, after the death of his father, he received the degree of *Magister Chemiae* from the University of Moscow and was elected extraor-dinary professor of analytical and organic chemistry in the Polytechnic Institute—ordinary professor from 1912—which post he occupied until the Polytechnic Institute was dis-banded in 1930. In 1912 he received the degree of *Doctor Chemiae* from the University of Dorpat. From 1921 on he was also professor of inorganic chemistry at the Polytechnic Institute and professor of chemistry at the Forestry Tech-nical Academy. From 1930 to 1934, after the dissolution of the Polytechnic Institute, he was professor of general chemistry at the Metallurgical Institute; and, after 1934, when that institute was combined with several others into the Industrial Institute, he was professor of general chem-istry at the Industrial Institute. After his father's death he lived with his mother, who died in September 1933 at the age of eighty-seven years. After that he lived alone until the time of his death in 1938.

Menshutkin is well known for his many chemical studies, the records of which constitute about one-third of all his publications. His textbooks, popular books, bibliographies, and so forth make up roughly another third, and his publications on the history of chemistry bring the list to about 220 items. His first published paper on an historical subject was written in 1894 while he was still a student. After that, for more than forty years he worked on the history of chemistry with the twofold objective of collecting material for a complete history of chemistry in Russia and of disseminating as widely as possible historical knowledge of chemistry in general. The first purpose he served by studies in archives, such as those of the Academy of Sciences and of the university, and by a study of the lives and works of eminent chemists, of their printed investigations, and of their letters and manuscripts; the second he served by his courses in the history of chemistry, by popular lectures, by books, and by articles in popular periodicals. His publications on Lomonosov constitute the twenty-seven items of the bibliography cited at the end of this book. No. 26 on this list is this same work which is here translated into English, the matured outcome of Menshutkin's long thinking and long study upon its subject. It is utterly authoritative, a book which will never have to be rewritten.

TENNEY L. DAVIS

September 1944   *Professor of Organic Chemistry*
Massachusetts Institute of Technology

CONTENTS

CONTENTS

RUSSIA'S LOMONOSOV

Mikhail Vasilyevich Lomonosov (1711-1765)

CHAPTER 1

The north of Russia in the seventeenth century—Arch-
angel and the Northern Dvina—The coast dwellers and
their occupation—Vasily Dorofeyev Lomonosov—The
first years of M. V. Lomonosov's life—Reading, writing,
and arithmetic—The influence of church books—De-
parture for Moscow—His life and studies at the Moscow
Slavo-Graeco-Latin Academy—The expedition of Kirillov
and the interrogation of Lomonosov—The trip to Kiev—
The founding of the Academy of Sciences at St. Peters-
burg—The Academic University and the arrival of Lo-
monosov in St. Petersburg—He is ordered abroad.

THE section of northern Russia bordering on the
White Sea, now such a hive of activity, played
an important role in the economic life of Russia
in the seventeenth and eighteenth centuries. It
is necessary to make this role quite clear so that the
appearance there at that time of a group of eminent Russians who had "come up from the people" can be understood. Of these the most talented and gifted was undoubtedly Mikhail Vasilyevich Lomonosov.

In the seventeenth century several historical causes contributed to the development of Russian culture in the north
on the White Sea and along the Northern Dvina with its
cities of Archangel and Kholmogory. At that time this
section was almost cut off from the rest of Russia—from
such cultural centers as Moscow and Kiev—by endless
swamps and dense forests which made intercommunication
difficult. But this remoteness and inaccessibility had several
centuries before saved the north of Russia from both the
Tartar yoke—it was never subjugated by the Tartars—and
from serfdom, a condition no less horrible. Hence the entire

population in the north, even in the cities, was always made up of peasants who had never been serfs.

From ancient times the northern region, thanks to its isolation, also had served as a refuge for fugitives from government persecution or from the oppression of serfdom, which became more unbearable in proportion to the extension of the power of the noble landowners over their serfs.

Thus the colonization of the north by peasants, religious dissenters, and Old Believers continued. Monasteries sprang up and played a powerful part in awakening the productive forces of the region during the fifteenth and sixteenth centuries. Detailed accounts have been preserved of highly important technical discoveries made in the sixteenth century by Philip, the abbot of the Solovetsky monastery. (He became metropolitan of Moscow and was eventually executed by Ivan the Terrible.)

Later a most extraordinary circumstance began to influence the development of the northern region. After direct trade relations with Western Europe were opened up in 1553, one may say that in the seventeenth and early eighteenth centuries all the foreign trade of Russia went through Archangel on the White Sea. This was almost the only port where English and other foreign ships discharged cargo. The foreigners first set up their factories there, and later in some other cities in the northern region. Since they lived there the year round, steady association with them could not but have some effect on the northerners who came into contact with them. The inhabitants' intellectual horizon broadened and they began to feel new needs, new ambitions. In spite of the fact that these foreigners were only trading folk, poorly educated and interested primarily in commercial profit, culturally they were nevertheless immeasurably superior to the Russians of that time. Meanwhile the delivery of foreign goods to Moscow and the trade in them became largely concentrated in the hands of the in-

AUTHOR'S PREFACE

THE 225th anniversary of the birth of M. V. Lomonosov was celebrated [in 1936] by the Soviet public with extraordinary unanimity and warmth. From Archangel to Stalingrad, from Minsk to Vladivostok, celebrations were organized in honor of the gifted Russian scholar and poet. Furthermore, so much information and discussion about Lomonosov appeared in the periodical press that the abundant festival literature of 1911 seems negligible by comparison.

The nationwide celebration of the memory of Lomonosov was a clear indication of the Soviet people's steadfast devotion to science. It shows their profound attachment to the cultural heritage of the past and their profound consciousness of their culture, now in the process of creation, which is national in form and socialistic in content. *Pravda* has epitomized our contemporary estimate of Lomonosov with full expressiveness and clarity in its lead article (No. 317, Nov. 18, 1936) entitled "The Gifted Son of the Great Russian People." Here he is called "the man whose legacy made a precious contribution to the permanent capital of Russian and of world culture." The article comments on "that high sense of dignity with which Lomonosov defended the rights of science." Finally, it stresses the passionate zeal with which Lomonosov struggled for the interests of the people by means of science and literature. "The extraordinary passion for a scientific knowledge of life and for a transformation of his native land gave strength to Lomonosov. Science for him was directly bound up with experience, with actual practice, with the industrial exploitation of the natural resources of the country, with the development of its productive powers and of its culture. He loved his people fervently. That is why he carried on so unremitting a struggle with the mere clerks of science, with the trade-guild scholars, shut off in a remote corner of their own narrow interests."

Hence also evolves Lomonosov's fight for the intelligibility and simplification of the literary language and for the ideological content of literature. "Soviet youth," says *Pravda*, "should be well acquainted with Lomonosov's life because of his great scientific zeal. His self-sacrificing struggle on behalf of science is one of the manifestations of the heroic character of the great Russian people."

Emerging from a young Russian culture that was only just then taking shape along European lines, Lomonosov was no mere student and imitative provincial. As an equal, freely and with an amazing sense of his own dignity and worth, he critically assimilated, adapted, and developed the great heritage of world culture. He was our first potential and outstanding contribution to the storehouse of world culture. The bourgeois culture of the West has passed by the prophecies and insights which are scattered so liberally and with such lavish generosity throughout the dissertations, speeches, and memoirs of the genius Lomonosov. He often found his opinions opposed on many points to those of the ruling classes. Always he put the interests of the whole Russian people foremost, the raising of the standard of living and the spread of education. His views on these matters were for his time so daring and so revolutionary that the papers and memoirs containing them were seized immediately after his death by order of the government.

The life and work of Lomonosov, the great patriot, the scholar-genius, the fervent champion of an original science and culture, are extremely instructive, indeed in our years especially for the rising generation. In this lies the significance of Lomonosov for our time and for our country.

The present account is a revised and enlarged version of the biography of Lomonosov which I wrote in 1911, commissioned by the presidium of the Academy of Sciences.

I have made use of new material which has come to light during the intervening twenty-five years and I have set forth some things in a way different from that which was possible under the earlier conditions of censorship.

In conclusion, let me mention the most important sources of information on the life and works of Lomonosov which I have used in preparing this book.

P. S. Bilyarsky, *Materialy dlya biografii Lomonosova (Material for a Biography of Lomonosov)* St. Petersburg, 1865.

P. P. Pekarsky, *Istoriya i. Akademii Nauk v Peterburge (History of the Imperial Academy of Sciences in St. Petersburg)* 2 vols., St. Petersburg, 1870, 1873.

A. Kunik, *Sbornik materialov dlya istorii i. Akademii Nauk v XVIII veke (Collection of Material for a History of the Imperial Academy of Sciences in the Eighteenth Century)* St. Petersburg, 1865.

Sochineniia M. V. Lomonosova (The Works of M. V. Lomonosov) published by the Academy of Sciences, 7 vols., St. Petersburg, 1891-1935.

Collections, published by the Academy of Sciences in 1911 and 1937.

B. N. Menshutkin, *Trudy M. V. Lomonosova po khimii i fizike (The Works of M. V. Lomonosov in Chemistry and Physics)* Leningrad, 1936.

L. B. Modzalevsky, *Rukopisi Lomonosova v Arkhive Akademii Nauk SSSR. Nauchnoe opisanie. (The Manuscripts of Lomonosov in the Archives of the Academy of Sciences of the U.S.S.R. A Scientific Account)* (In press).[1]

[1] In 1937. ED.

population in the north, even in the cities, was always made up of peasants who had never been serfs.

From ancient times the northern region, thanks to its isolation, also had served as a refuge for fugitives from government persecution or from the oppression of serfdom, which became more unbearable in proportion to the extension of the power of the noble landowners over their serfs.

Thus the colonization of the north by peasants, religious dissenters, and Old Believers continued. Monasteries sprang up and played a powerful part in awakening the productive forces of the region during the fifteenth and sixteenth centuries. Detailed accounts have been preserved of highly important technical discoveries made in the sixteenth century by Philip, the abbot of the Solovetsky monastery. (He became metropolitan of Moscow and was eventually executed by Ivan the Terrible.)

Later a most extraordinary circumstance began to influence the development of the northern region. After direct trade relations with Western Europe were opened up in 1553, one may say that in the seventeenth and early eighteenth centuries all the foreign trade of Russia went through Archangel on the White Sea. This was almost the only port where English and other foreign ships discharged cargo. The foreigners first set up their factories there, and later in some other cities in the northern region. Since they lived there the year round, steady association with them could not but have some effect on the northerners who came into contact with them. The inhabitants' intellectual horizon broadened and they began to feel new needs, new ambitions. In spite of the fact that these foreigners were only trading folk, poorly educated and interested primarily in commercial profit, culturally they were nevertheless immeasurably superior to the Russians of that time. Meanwhile the delivery of foreign goods to Moscow and the trade in them became largely concentrated in the hands of the in-

CHAPTER 1

The north of Russia in the seventeenth century—Arch-
angel and the Northern Dvina—The coast dwellers and
their occupation—Vasily Dorofeyev Lomonosov—The
first years of M. V. Lomonosov's life—Reading, writing,
and arithmetic—The influence of church books—De-
parture for Moscow—His life and studies at the Moscow
Slavo-Graeco-Latin Academy—The expedition of Kirillov
and the interrogation of Lomonosov—The trip to Kiev—
The founding of the Academy of Sciences at St. Peters-
burg—The Academic University and the arrival of Lo-
monosov in St. Petersburg—He is ordered abroad.

THE section of northern Russia bordering on the
White Sea, now such a hive of activity, played
an important role in the economic life of Russia
in the seventeenth and eighteenth centuries. It
is necessary to make this role quite clear so that the
appearance there at that time of a group of eminent Russians who had "come up from the people" can be understood. Of these the most talented and gifted was undoubtedly Mikhail Vasilyevich Lomonosov.

In the seventeenth century several historical causes contributed to the development of Russian culture in the north
on the White Sea and along the Northern Dvina with its
cities of Archangel and Kholmogory. At that time this
section was almost cut off from the rest of Russia—from
such cultural centers as Moscow and Kiev—by endless
swamps and dense forests which made intercommunication
difficult. But this remoteness and inaccessibility had several
centuries before saved the north of Russia from both the
Tartar yoke—it was never subjugated by the Tartars—and
from serfdom, a condition no less horrible. Hence the entire

Mikhail Vasilyevich Lomonosov (1711-1765)

habitants of the White Sea region. This not only developed an enterprising spirit among them but also gave them many contacts with the cultural attainments of the Russian capital. As the quest for business profit continued to lure many folk to the north, the population of the Northern Dvina region increased rapidly.

Another important factor contributing to the spread of culture was the influence of convicts. The northern region had always served as a place of banishment for those who were *persona non grata* to the tsarist government. As is well known, in the sixteenth and seventeenth centuries individuals who ranked high in society or in service to the court, not infrequently the foremost people in the Russia of that day, suffered exile.

When Peter I came to the throne his repeated visits to the north also did much to awaken the social life of the population.

Briefly enumerated, the foregoing are the chief factors that stimulated the broad cultural activity of the White Sea region, which centered for the most part in Archangel and Kholmogory, and attained its highest development early in the eighteenth century. About the year 1670, in the Antonievo-Siisky monastery, ninety-six kilometers from Kholmogory on the Northern Dvina, a printing office was opened, and the monastery became a center which attracted the educated people of that section.

Early in the eighteenth century a theological seminary was founded at Kholmogory, books circulated among the peasants of the province, and some of them began to collect libraries of moderate size. In addition there was a school of icon painters, in which there were some real portrait artists, at the Antonievo-Siisky monastery.

To complete the picture of life in the northern region, something must be said about the coast dwellers who lived mainly along the banks of the Dvina and of the Onega and on the coast of the White Sea. These people gained their livelihood by shipping. In the spring, after the rivers and sea were open, they departed in their ships, most often to the Murmansk shore. There they worked all through the short northern summer, and in the autumn returned to their native forests with their profit. Their occupation was difficult and dangerous; often, even in summer, the northern seas were filled with icebergs, and frequent violent storms and heavy fogs forced the coast dwellers to be ever ready for emergency. All this so tempered their character as to make them a resolute dauntless people.

On returning home the coast dweller became a trader. All through the winter huge caravans laden with fish and other sea produce made their way from the White Sea region to Moscow, returning later with wares needed by the northerners. Even in the seventeenth century some of the most enterprising coast dwellers began to carry on trading operations beyond the limits of Russia, in neighboring Norway and even in England. Thus, in general, the coast dwellers constituted an independent group in the population (although they always considered themselves peasants) distinguished by their industry and their high level of development.

The coast dwellers' business required special equipment—seagoing ships, fishing tackle, various provisions such as salt for curing fish, and the like. To meet these needs dockyards and factories had long existed on the Northern Dvina. One of the largest dockyards in the beginning of the eighteenth century was the Vavchuzhsky, belonging to the brothers Bazhenov. Situated eight kilometers to the east of Kholmogory, it built not only fishing boats, but also merchant ships and even warships. Near the dockyard were well-equipped spinning and sail factories and sawmills operated by water power. Salt for preserving fish was also prepared on the spot. Salt boilers, working mostly in winter and obtaining salt from seawater, were located in many places on the seacoast. Such was the general condition of the White Sea region in the beginning of the eighteenth century.

The topography of Lomonosov's native land deserves brief mention. Eighty kilometers from Archangel, just where the Northern Dvina flows into the White Sea, the river branches out into a number of arms which form many islands and islets. Each of these arms has its own name, such as Kholmogorka, Rovdogorka, Bystrokurka, and so on, as has every island. On one of these islands, ten kilometers from where the Northern Dvina begins to split into branches, is situated the city of Kholmogory. Facing it to the east, on the river Kholmogorka, is Kurostrov. There, in the beginning of the eighteenth century, were as many as twenty villages, settled almost exclusively by coast dwellers and encircling the highland center of Kurostrov. In one of these, the village of Denisovka, lived Vasily Dorofeyev Lomonosov, the father of the future scholar and academician.

Vasily Dorofeyev was a typical coast dweller of his time and one of the most well-to-do and enterprising. He owned several ships and traded on the Murmansk shore, but often, in quest of profit, penetrated far into the Arctic Ocean. A pioneer among the coast folk, he was the first to build a new ship there and rig it in the European manner. It was a galiot of considerable size named the *Sea Gull*. Ownership of such vessels enabled him to engage in the transport of government supplies and private goods from Archangel to Pustozersk, Solovky, Kola, and on the river Mezen and along the shore of Lapland. At that time he owned a considerable amount of land. Thus he was able to accumulate substantial wealth. This is indicated by the fact that the Dmitrievsky stone church at Kurostrov was built chiefly with money which he contributed.

Vasily Dorofeyev's only son, Mikhailo Vasilyevich, was born in 1711 to his wife by his first marriage, Yelena Ivanovna Sivkovka, daughter of the deacon of the village of Nikolayevsk Matigory. The exact day of his birth is unknown, but accepted opinion sets it as the eighth of November. The education of young Lomonosov differed in no way from that given to other coastland children. Until the age of ten he remained in the village. Then his father began to take him out on business every year so that he might be trained from youth to assume the responsibilities which would be his when his father grew old. These voyages continued until Lomonosov was almost nineteen years old. During these years he made himself thoroughly conversant with the life of the coast dwellers, learned about shipbuilding and the manufacture of salt and other coastal products, and became acquainted with the most diverse areas of north Russia. Even then Lomonosov, the future scholar, revealed himself. Everywhere he made careful observations, noticed all the details of his surroundings, and retained exact recollections of what he saw. Although it is known that he could not have traveled in the northern seas after 1730, here, for example, is what he writes in one of his letters of 1761: "The Lapps are distinguished both by poor growth and weakness because they rarely eat bread and meat, feeding almost exclusively on fish. I, being then fourteen, towered above and outweighed strong Lapps of thirty. Even though they are always sunburned in summer and do not know either rouge or white paint, when I chanced to see them naked I was surprised at their whiteness, in which they surpass the freshest codfish, their chief daily food."

During the winter Lomonosov spent with his books all the time he had free from business duties. From his early years he had studied reading and writing with Ivan Shubny, his neighbor in the village, and later probably studied with the deacon of the village church, S. N. Sabelnikov. I. I.

Lepehkin writes: "Even as a twelve-year-old boy he loved to read the Psalms and services in church and, in accordance with the custom here, the Lives of the Saints as printed in the Prologues. In this he was very clever and endowed with a profound memory. When he had read some biography or discourse, after the chanting he would recite it accurately in shortened form to the old men sitting in the refectory." Undoubtedly in these youthful years Lomonosov became much occupied with religious matters because of the influence of ecclesiastical and other religious books—the only ones he had at his disposal. Another influence was that of the religious dissenters and Old Believers, who were very numerous at that time in the Northern Dvina region and were naturally very much preoccupied with discussions on the "true faith."

According to some authorities, Lomonosov also joined one of the sects (the one which recognized no priests) and remained a member for two years. His later literary works show that the widely circulated rhymed religious books of Simeon Polotsky, the *Psaltery*, the *Garden of Many Colors*, and the *Rhythmologion*, made an especially strong impression on him.

However, as far as we are able to judge, the attraction of religion did not last long. About 1725 Lomonosov was able to obtain his first nonreligious books from one of the villagers, Christofor Dudin. These were the *Slavic Grammar* of Smotritsky and Magnitsky's *Arithmetic*. Smotritsky's *Grammar* went through a series of editions in the seventeenth century and was considered at the time the best book of its type. Grammar, defined as "the well-known art of teaching how to read and write well," was a broader subject than it now is. The *Grammar* was provided with a prosody in which were explained the rules "of the meter or quantitative measure of the composition of verses." The *Arithmetic* of Magnitsky, published in Moscow in 1703, was "for the sake of the instruction of wisdom-loving boys and girls." It represented not only what we would now consider a book on arithmetic, but also a popularly expounded collection of all sorts of exact and natural sciences: geometry, physics, geography, astronomy, and so on. All of this information was so presented as to apply to the Russian life of this time, and in such a way that the reader could understand everything without a teacher if only he were industrious and zealous. Magnitsky's point of view was expressed in the maxim, "the faculty of speech and writing should be drilled in the knowledge and glorification of God."

These two books probably also had a decisive significance in directing Lomonosov's intellectual activity toward the exact sciences. But it was not easy for him to pursue them. His father married again in 1725, for the third time, to Irina Semyonovna Korelskaya of Nikolayevsk Matigory. This second stepmother was not well disposed toward Lomonosov. As he himself writes: "Although I had a father who was a good man by nature, though brought up in the utmost ignorance, I had a wicked and jealous stepmother who tried in every way to arouse anger in my father. She made out that I was always idly sitting at my books so that I was constantly obliged to read and study what I could in solitary and desolate places, and to suffer cold and hunger."

Later, people who knew (Lomonosov's closest relatives at that time were serving in the Archangel customhouse) explained to him that in order to study science it was indispensable, first of all, to learn the Latin language, through which at that time all scholars communicated, in which scientific books were written almost exclusively, and by means of which all teaching was conducted. But it was impossible for Lomonosov to study this language in his native land. Although a Slavo-Latin School was founded in Kholmogory in 1723 by the Archbishop Varnava, as a general rule peasants subjected to a poll tax, as was Lomonosov, were not admitted.

Oppressive family tyranny, constant outbursts by the second stepmother against the "ne'er-do-well" Lomonosov, brought him to a decision to leave his family and try to obtain elsewhere by his own efforts the knowledge and education he desired. Quite naturally his thoughts settled on Moscow, the center of the cultural life of the day, where it would be easiest to realize his ambition. As already pointed out, the active trade relations of the Northern Dvina region with the capital of the time, then only beginning to yield its supremacy to the young St. Petersburg, naturally resulted in the constant presence there of many coast dwellers. They had lived there a long time, knew the city well, and had their offices and shops there. The clerks of these shops were sent as escorts of the long winter wagon trains of goods. Undoubtedly Lomonosov was able to learn from them all that interested him.

He realized his aims at the end of the year 1730. We have documentary evidence on the subject, for in the record of the Kurostrov district is the following memorandum: "In 1730, on the seventh day of December, Mikhailo Vasilyev Lomonosov was allowed to go to Moscow and to the sea until the month of September of the following year, 1731, and Ivan Banev signed the guarantee of payment of his poll tax."

Further on, another statement, which is provided by Lomonosov himself, will be adduced as to the circumstances of his departure from Denisovka. He interrupted his journey for a few days at the Antonievo-Siisky monastery, where he served temporarily as psalm reader. From there he set out directly with one of the numerous caravans which was hastening to make use of the established sledge route to deliver goods to Moscow. Lomonosov arrived in Moscow in the middle of January. He stayed with a fellow villager, the clerk Pyatukhin, and immediately petitioned for admission to one of the Moscow schools. At first he tried to settle in the accounting school (the school of navigation, according to other sources). But at the end of January he submitted to Archimandrite Herman of the Zaikonospassky monastery a petition for admission to the Moscow Slavo-Graeco-Latin Academy connected with the monastery.

In order to be enrolled, Lomonosov concealed his peasant origin in the examination and represented himself to be the son of a nobleman of Kholmogory. In a decree of the synod of July 7, 1723, an order had been promulgated "to dismiss and henceforth not to admit people belonging to estate owners and the sons of peasants, as well as the stupid and the malignant." Evidently they did not demand an immediate presentation of full proof of Lomonosov's noble origin and admitted him to the academy.

A higher institution of learning in the early eighteenth century had little in common with what we are now accustomed to understand by that appellation. The Slavo-Graeco-Latin Academy, founded in 1684, consisted of eight classes: four lower ones (grammar, syntax); two middle classes (poetry, rhetoric) and two higher (philosophy, religion). The instruction in the lower classes was concentrated chiefly on the study of Latin, learned so thoroughly that at the end of the fourth year the students could read and write it, and on the study of the Slavonic language. In addition, they had to know geography, history, the catechism, and arithmetic. In the middle classes, the students were already obliged to speak Latin. The students' scholarship was entrusted to auditors chosen from the most diligent pupils, and then later to teachers. General recitations were conducted on Saturdays, when the lazy were subjected to floggings.

The middle classes, poetry and rhetoric, were for a time devoted to prosody, composition, and eloquence, and then to the chief subject, theology: the older classes also were given up to religion and philosophy. Once they had progressed into the upper classes, the pupils were made "students" and finished the course as "learned theologians." Thus the academy was, essentially, a specialized theological faculty.

Lomonosov's position in the academy was a fairly difficult one, and only his unquenchable thirst for learning enabled him to endure the severe environment in which he was obliged to study. In one of his letters he describes his life in the academy in the following terms: "When studying in the Spassky School I was subjected on all sides to powerful influences, which in those years were almost irresistible, hindering me from knowledge. On the one hand, my father, having no other children than myself, said that I, being the only one, had abandoned him and had abandoned all the fortune (measured by local conditions) which he had amassed for me by bloody sweat and which, after his death, others would plunder. On the other hand, there was inexpressible poverty: since I had only an altyn [three kopeks] a day for wages, I could not have more for food each day than half a kopek's worth of bread and half a kopek's worth of kvas, and the rest for paper, shoes, and other necessities. In such a manner I lived for five years and never abandoned learning. On the one hand they wrote that, knowing my father's means, the good people at home set their daughters' caps for me—they had proposed even while I was yet there. On the other hand, the schoolboys, little children, used to cry out and point at me with their fingers, 'Look, what a blockhead to be studying Latin at twenty!' "

Lomonosov's astounding talents were not slow in making themselves felt. He went through the first three classes in one year, during which he applied himself especially to Latin. At the end of a year he could compose Latin poems of moderate length. However, he obviously could not find

in the academy what he so yearned for, the exact sciences.
The longer he remained there and the more he developed,
the less it satisfied him; he felt no inclination toward those
scholastic and theological sciences which alone made up
the curriculum. This spiritual dissatisfaction, together with
the impossibility of approaching the goals he had projected
and his extremely difficult material circumstances (the state
scholarship was only an altyn a day—and outside presents
amounted barely to a few rubles a year) compelled him to
search for a chance to change his position. Such an opportunity came in 1734.

Early in the eighteenth century the expansion of Russian
dominions to the southeast was in progress. In 1734 the
government equipped an expedition under the leadership of
I. K. Kirillov and Colonel Tevkelev to secure the eastern
frontier definitely. With this in view it was proposed to
found a new city (the present Orenburg) in order both to
enter into trade relations as actively as possible with the
inhabitants of the province and to spread Orthodoxy among
them. To realize the latter aim, an indispensable member of
the expedition, in addition to "officers, artillerymen, engi-
neers, naval officers, and other people of varied ranks," had
to be a learned priest of the Slavo-Graeco-Latin Academy;
hence all the "learned" priests in Moscow at the time received an invitation to join the expedition. Not one of
them, however, was favorably disposed toward leaving the
capital to go into the hinterland, and all declined the opportunity. Thereupon Kirillov appealed to the archimandrite
of the Zaikonospassky monastery with the proposal that one
of the students of the older classes be ordained as a priest.
Lomonosov turned out to be the one who was willing.

Again at the "candidate's table" of the Slavo-Graeco-
Latin Academy, Lomonosov was subjected to a detailed
cross-examination on his origin, since at that time they
were very strict on the point that only those possessing

legal qualifications should be made priests. This time, on September 4, 1734, "he said in the questioning that his father was the priest Vasily Dorofeyev of the Church of the Presentation of the Most Holy Mother of God in Kholmogory, and that he, Mikhailo, had lived with his father and had never lived elsewhere, had not enlisted as a dragoon or a soldier or in the service of Her Imperial Majesty, had not been sent into exile with the carpenters; that he had been correctly recorded as the real son of his father and was exempt from taxes. He had separated from his father to go to Moscow in the first days of December 1730. Having arrived in Moscow in the month of January 1731, he was enrolled in the above-mentioned academy, where he had since remained and had progressed as far as rhetoric in his studies. He, Mikhailo, being still unmarried, was only twenty-three years old. . . . He had no heresy, sickness, deafness, or injury in any members. . . . He could write cursively. And in case he had spoken falsely, then his priestly rank should be taken from him, he should be shaven, and be sent into cruel servitude in a distant monastery.

"To this examination the student of the Moscow Slavo-Graeco-Latin Academy, Mikhailo Lomonosov, has set his hand."

But the matter did not end here. Lomonosov's declaration was immediately subjected to verification by the board (*Kammerkollegia*) and there he testified to the whole truth about himself. "He was born, [he said,] Mikhailo, in the province of Archangel, in the Dvina district, in the canton of Kurostrov, the son of the peasant Vasily Dorofeyev, and his father was residing even then in the same village with other peasants and was subject to the poll tax. But in the past year, 1730, with his said father's permission, he Lomonosov, had departed for Moscow, for which purpose a passport had been given him (which he had lost through carelessness) from the chancellery of the governor of Kholmogory, at the hand of Gregory Vorobeyev, governor at the time. And with that passport, he said, he had come to Moscow, and lived, at the order of the police, with the clerk Ivan Dutikov from January to the last days of 1731, until exactly what date he did not remember. And in those days he had submitted a petition to Archimandrite Herman of the Zaikonospassky monastery (now most reverend archbishop of Archangel and Kholmogory) that he should be taken into the school. After the archimandrite had accepted him in accordance with this petition, he had ordered that he be examined, which he was. And that he, Lomonosov, had declared in this examination that he was the son of a nobleman of the city of Kholmogory. And, in accordance with the examination, he, the archimandrite, had had him, Mikhailo, admitted to the school, where he reached the grade of rhetoric. And that he, Mikhailo, had wished to go voluntarily on the expedition with the state councillor, Ivan Kirillov. And that he had called himself a priest's son in the candidate's chair, and that he had done this in his innocence not expecting that thereby there would be cause or obstacle to his being received into the priesthood—and no one had taught him to say he was a priest's son. And now he wished to study in the academy as before. And in this interrogation he had told the real truth, without lies or concealment—and if he had concealed anything, then there should be inflicted on him, Lomonosov, whatever the administration of the Moscow synod should decree."

Quite as would be expected after Lomonosov's real origin was discovered, any possibility of his promotion to the priesthood or of his participation in the Orenburg expedition fell through. Expulsion from the academy was threatened him, but it did not take place, evidently because he enjoyed the good will of all the persons in authority. That much is clear not only from the fact that the inquiry remained without harmful consequences for him, but also that, in answer to a special petition from Lomonosov, the archimandrite ordered him to Kiev after (in December 1734) he had entered the class in philosophy. He was to stay there a year to complete his education in the Kiev Ecclesiastical Academy, then considered the foremost of the Russian educational institutions. In Kiev, however, Lomonosov found nothing that was not theological and, thoroughly dissatisfied, returned to Moscow before the year elapsed to finish his education there.

But Lomonosov was not to become a learned cleric. At the end of 1735 an extraordinary event occurred which severed immediately his connection with the Slavo-Graeco-Latin Academy and fully satisfied all his aspirations in a way which he had probably never dreamed. His stay in the academy was fruitful in that, besides providing Latin and other studies, it enabled him to make up to some degree what he lacked—a general education—and logic and philosophy contributed to that clarity of thinking and exposition which is manifest in all his scientific works.

The cause of the unexpected change in Lomonosov's position lay in St. Petersburg at the Academy of Sciences, which had been founded some years before and with which he was inseparably connected from that time until his death. The Academy of Sciences owed its origin to Peter the Great, who discussed the possibility of founding it with the famous philosopher Leibnitz as early as 1711-1716. However, not until 1720 did Peter take steps to realize his plans, concerning which he wrote to Leibnitz's closest colleague, the philosopher Christian von Wolf, whom he knew personally.

Wolf (1679-1754) became professor of mathematics and natural sciences at Halle in 1707. An outstanding scholar, he brought clarity and accuracy to every subject he taught. In 1723 he was suddenly dismissed from office for freethinking, and had to leave Prussia within two days. He traveled to Marburg, outside the boundaries of Prussia, and was made a professor in the university there. He remained in this city seventeen years and then, having received a full pardon, returned to Halle in 1740, where he was professor of natural philosophy until his death. During his life he wrote some dozens of books on philosophy, various branches of the natural sciences, physics, mechanics, and so on.

It was to him that Peter I assigned the difficult task of inviting the first members of the Academy of Sciences in 1724, when plans for the new academy took more concrete form in the project of the physician-in-ordinary L. L. Blumentrost. Since there were no qualified scientists in Russia at that time, it was necessary to invite them from abroad. Wolf performed his arduous task with distinction. He was able to gather together distinguished scholars, especially in the field of mathematics, and the new academy at once occupied an honorable position among the European institutions of its type.

Those few years in the life of the academy during which Peter I and Catherine I reigned were the years of its flowering. But when Peter II ascended the throne the capital was moved back to Moscow and the academy fell upon evil days. For years at a time it received no grants of money and was obliged to carry on its numerous institutions—printing office, typefoundry, graver's plant, workshop for making precision instruments, and the like—as best it could by running into debt. Since the academy had no officially ratified statutes, all power in it belonged to the chancellery, of which the director (and librarian) was Johann Daniel Schumacher, the actual head of the entire academy. The gymnasium and university also declined during this period, since many families had moved to Moscow in the wake of the court. In 1734 I. A. Korff was appointed chief director of the Academy of Sciences. He was an energetic man who had done everything he could to better the condition of the academy. In order to fill up the gymnasium and the university, he petitioned the senate in 1735 to issue a decree requiring that students with sufficient preparation to listen to the professors' lectures be sent from the monasteries and the schools of Russia to the gymnasium of the academy.

The senate issued a decree in conformity with this petition, and among other things the rector of the Zaikono-spassky academy was instructed to choose and send to St. Petersburg twenty students in the eminent sciences. However, they found only twelve in all of such students, since the best scholars were quickly snatched up from the senior classes by the hospital and other institutions. These students, "in our opinion by no means of the least keenness of mind," as the archimandrite wrote, were outfitted for the road. The best of all of them was Mikhailo Lomonosov. They left Moscow on December 23, 1735, and arrived in St. Petersburg on New Year's Day, 1736; they were enrolled at once as students of the University of St. Petersburg and immediately began their studies. Thus was the opportunity to study the exact sciences presented to Lomonosov.

However, this was little in comparison with what awaited him in the very near future. A great exploring expedition from the academy was then at work in Siberia. The foremost representatives of the natural sciences were members of the expedition, but there was no chemist who was also acquainted with metallurgy and mining. No foreigners of this type were available, at least not any who wished to travel to Russia. Therefore, on the advice of one of the well-known metallurgists of Germany, I. Henckel of Freiberg, Baron Korff, the chief director of the academy, decided to send him three students best prepared to study chemistry and metallurgy. The academy selected three Muscovites, Lomonosov, Vinogradov, and the son of the mining councillor, Reiser. When the elder Reiser learned of this, like a practical man he pointed out to Baron Korff the necessity of acquainting the chosen students in at least an elementary way with those theoretical subjects on which metallurgy and mining are based: mathematics, mechanics, physics, philosophy, and chemistry. This intelligent suggestion was adopted and, having changed its original decision, the academy resolved to send the students to Marburg to learn the elements of the necessary basic sciences. They were to go to Professor Christian Wolf, who gave his consent to their instruction in the University of Marburg.

A mission abroad was a complicated matter in those days. Notwithstanding the provision made by the cabinet of ministers as early as March 13, 1736, to send three students abroad with a stipend of 1,200 rubles a year, and in spite of all efforts to make haste, the actual departure of the young men did not take place until autumn of that year. They were given explicit instructions concerning such matters as the selection of men with whom they were to study, their personal behavior, and the handling of their money. Every six months they were required to send reports to the academy on their progress in their studies, their expenditures, and the like.

The sea voyage took considerable time. Because of the autumn storms, the ship *Ferbotot* first was delayed a long while in sailing from St. Petersburg and later remained several days at Kronstadt, from which port it finally set out on September 23. After a stormy voyage, it arrived at Travemunde on October 16. The students, following a few days' rest at Lubeck, continued their journey by post through Hamburg, Minden, and Cassel to Marburg, where they were met by Professor Wolf on November 3.

CHAPTER 2

Lomonosov's stay in Marburg—The physics of Professor Wolf—Studies in the sciences—Courses in chemistry—Lomonosov's success in his studies—The students' debts—Lomonosov's stay in Freiberg under Henckel—Lomonosov's wanderings and his marriage—His return to St. Petersburg—His appointment as adjunct of the academy—Lomonosov's behavior in the academy and his arrest—His labors and repentance—His appointment as professor of chemistry—The chair of chemistry in the academy—Public lectures in physics—The equipment of the chemical laboratory at the Academy of Sciences.

NO OTHER period of Lomonosov's life is known so well or in such detail as his stay abroad. Constant reports, the letters of Wolf, Henckel, Lomonosov himself, and Reiser make it possible to reconstruct all the details of our students' sojourn in Marburg and Freiberg. A considerable part of these dispatches is devoted to the personal side of their life, the scandals and other disturbing events which occurred in the quiet German town through the initiative of our young men—affairs which were chiefly the responsibility of the European celebrity, Professor Wolf, to settle some way or other.

We can quite appreciate their jolly life. I have described the typical fare in Moscow at the Slavo-Graeco-Latin Academy. In the St. Petersburg University conditions were rather better, to be sure, but still far from perfect, and in any case supervision was unremitting. Now in Marburg strict rules and poverty were replaced by the free atmosphere of a German university and, for that time, lavish means—about 4,000 gold rubles a year for each student. Drinking bouts, revels, and brawls became frequent occurrences with them.

In these indulgences Lomonosov did not lag behind his fellows, but, in contrast to them, as soon as he had become familiar with the German language—and he did so speedily —he worked zealously at his studies. Christian Wolf himself taught our students philosophy, physics, and mechanics; they studied mathematics and chemistry with Professor Duising. Wolf's lectures exercised an enormous influence on Lomonosov and, beyond doubt, determined his future scientific work.

It may not be amiss at this point to say something about the content of Wolf's course in physics in its general outlines. It will serve to show the state of this science in the first half of the eighteenth century and allow us to grasp the genius with which Lomonosov later worked out his own original points of view on the groundwork of the general physical and philosophical views of his teacher.[1]

Wolf divides physics into the experimental and the theoretical. The first is the science of everything that can be learned through experimentation; the second, the knowledge of everything that proceeds from the essence and properties of substances. To alter substances, external force, which can act only by means of motion and its laws, is necessary. All that physics affirms is based on experiment and observation, and only what proceeds directly therefrom can be regarded as the truth. Conjectures are only tolerated when they lead to further observations and experiments. A body which has extension consists of matter and may be divided into incomprehensibly small parts. Between such particles in substances there are crevices, so that every kind of physical substance consists of crevices and real particles. The matter of substances may be their own plus outside

[1] He translated into Russian the first part of Wolf's *Physics* (*Volfianskaya Eksperimentalnaya Fizika*), printed in 1746; the second part (*Teoreticheskaya Sokrashchennaya Fizika*) was translated under his supervision by Boris Volkov in 1760.

matter which freely passes through the crevices of the former. Besides these there may be variable matter contained in the large openings of the substance itself (air or water, for instance). All of these forms of matter are in the shape of very small particles. The number of simple forms of matter which constitute them is now unknown, since many of them are invisible, like the stuff of fire, light, gravity, or magnetism. Matter proper exhibits such properties as hardness, strength, coarseness, and roughness. The volume of bodies depends on the quantity of variable matter, while their fluidity (the particles moving apart through the action of the heat matter), their heat, their weight (effect of gravity matter), and their elasticity (effect of elastic matter) all depend on the outside matter.

Heat consists of the movement of very delicate matter passing from one body to another. This external heat producing matter when in a state of rest does not heat bodies. Light is diffused by the movement, communicated by a luminous body to the light matter which flows through the entire universe. The motion is spread by a series of identical little elastic spheres which are in contact with one another: this is the "world ether." The elasticity of its particles depends on the elastic matter present in the openings between the particles of ether. Electric phenomena are produced by a fluid subtle matter, probably the same as the matter of light and fire, that is, ether.

Such were Wolf's views on the most important questions of physics, which I have described as far as possible with the expressions used by Lomonosov in his translation of Wolf's *Physics*. In them we see the typical physics of that time (and much later) when the existence of separate, very delicate, all-penetrating fluid substances was accepted to explain the phenomena of heat, light, and the like.

In his teaching Wolf adhered rigidly to the mathematical method, which made for order, clarity, and precision in the

elucidation of such branches of science as physics. Lomonosov profoundly respected his teacher and always maintained
good relations with him. In his notes he remarked that he
was under great obligation to Wolf, while in one of his
letters to L. Euler he said that he was refraining from pub-
lishing certain works lest he distress Wolf.

Chemistry, the other chief subject which Lomonosov
studied in Marburg, was taught by Professor Duising, a
rather commonplace professor it would seem. Early in the
second quarter of the eighteenth century the inductive
method of reasoning, which had been gradually working its
way into the exact sciences since the seventeenth century,
still had little to do with chemistry. In inductive reasoning,
experimentation and the conclusions drawn from it are
paramount, and conjectures or hypotheses are made only
to explain the results of experimentation. In the period now
under consideration there was a tendency to reduce all explanations of chemical phenomena to one hypothetical substance, phlogiston. Chemistry was under the influence of
the phlogiston theory, which persisted until the end of the
eighteenth century, chiefly because chemical changes were
studied only qualitatively to the neglect of their quantitative
aspects.

The principle of combustion was called phlogiston, and it
was thought that all substances capable of burning, or of
being altered by the action of fire, contained this substance.
Credit for the chief development of the theory of phlogiston
belongs to the German chemist E. Stahl, who died in 1734.
According to this theory, the process of the burning (calcination) of metal in air—tin or lead for example—consists in
this: the phlogiston leaves the metal and the dross (calx)
remains. Consequently it was assumed that tin or any other
combustible metal consists of calx and phlogiston and thus
represents a complex substance. The easier and the more
intense the phenomena of combustion, the greater the

amount of phlogiston in the burning body, therefore coal was considered most rich in it—practically pure phlogiston. Phlogiston itself was for Stahl a hypothetical element, but its existence was held to be beyond question. In it we have a substance quite similar to the intangible and imperceptible "fluids" of heat, light, elasticity, and the like, the acceptance of which was so widespread at that time.

Regardless of its falsity, the theory of phlogiston contributed its share to the development of chemistry. It initiated the adoption of a new method of investigation which enriched chemistry by a series of new facts, especially in the pursuit of those goals which Stahl expressed in the definition of chemistry as "the art of reducing complex substances into their component parts and of reconstructing them from these component parts." Later, when we examine Lomonosov's labors in chemistry, I shall say something in more detail about phlogiston and some other characteristic peculiarities of the chemistry of the first half of the eighteenth century.

In his last year of study, 1738-1739, Lomonosov, under Wolf's direction, became acquainted with the works of the most outstanding philosophers, physicists, and chemists of the seventeenth and the first part of the eighteenth century. Worthy of mention is Hermann Boerhaave's *Elementa Chemiae*, one of the best such works of its time, in which the chief emphasis is on the practical side of the art of chemistry, and phlogiston is not mentioned. Lomonosov makes constant use of this book in his works and quotes it very frequently in the dissertations which he sent to the Academy of Sciences as reports on his scientific studies. Also of interest is the sketch in Lomonosov's own hand which he sent in 1739 as an example of the progress he had made in drawing.[2]

In accordance with his instructions, Lomonosov also re-

[2] This sketch has been included in the book of L. B. Modzalevsky.

ported on the progress of his academic studies. As a demonstration of his exercises in the Russian and French languages he sent a rhymed translation, *Ode, composed by M. François de Salignac de La Mothe Fénelon, Archbishop Duke of Cambrai, Prince of the Holy Roman Empire*, which begins with the lines:

> The mountains that audacious-wise,
> Clad changelessly in ice and snow,
> That toward the very stars upthrow
> A shaft inviolate to the skies.

This was Lomonosov's first poem written in metric form.

It is specially important to mention the profound impression made on Lomonosov by the works of the very famous English natural philosopher Robert Boyle (1627-1691). The labors of this scholar, in which he investigated the properties of those invisible particles that make up all substances, captivated Lomonosov and determined the direction of his scientific activity. In one of his memoranda, referring to the year 1756, Lomonosov writes: "After I had read through Boyle, a passionate desire to investigate the minute particles of substances took possession of me. For eighteen years I had pondered over them; it is not my habit to begin to think about a subject only when the time has already come to explain it." In another memorandum he sets forth the full importance of such an investigation: "If I wished to read without knowing my letters, it would be absurd. In just the same way, if I wished to deliberate on natural subjects without having any conception of their origins, it would be just as senseless." Finally, it was from Boyle that Lomonosov derived the idea that it was necessary to study the minute particles with the help of mathematics, physics, and chemistry. He expresses this thought in the manner of Boyle, thus: "Chemistry is the right hand of physics: mathematics, its eyes, since it points out the way to accurate judgment."

During their three years in Marburg, the students had mastered the theoretical fundamentals of the exact sciences sufficiently well and Christian Wolf gave the following opinion of Lomonosov's progress (I am giving Lomonosov's translation): "A young man of superior capacity, Mikhailo Lomonosov, from the time when he arrived at Marburg frequently attended my lectures, chiefly in physics, but also in mathematics and philosophy. He had a passion for thorough study. If he carries on henceforth with the same eagerness, then I do not doubt that on returning to his fatherland he will, as I wish from the bottom of my heart, bring to it, considerable benefits." With like enthusiasm, Professor Duising reported that Lomonosov attended his lectures in chemistry with indefatigable diligence and, he was convinced, derived a great deal of benefit thereby. Meanwhile Lomonosov had already become acquainted with French and drawing, which, as we shall see, were also to become very useful to him in the future.

Even in the second year of our young men's stay in Marburg, the letters of Christian Wolf reveal that rumors had begun to come to him concerning the debts they had contracted. In consequence, the strictest instructions were sent to the students from the Academy of Sciences under no circumstances to contract debts. But, probably because of the great distance, these instructions produced no results and everything went on as before. When in July 1739 the time came for them to gather up their effects and travel to Freiberg to be with Henckel, the metallurgist, the creditors descended upon Professor Wolf. The amount of the debts had piled up until it had finally reached the sum of 1,936 thalers (about 12,000 gold rubles). It was Wolf's responsibility to pay them off as best he could, which he did in part from his own pocket (that amount was later refunded to him by the academy). Here is what he wrote to Baron Korff on the day following the departure of Lomonosov and his companions: "The students left here, departing from my house shortly after five o'clock in the morning on the twentieth of July. As each entered the carriage, he was provided with money for his traveling expenses. I had to take numerous precautions to prevent clashes between Vinogradov and certain students who would have delayed his departure. Lomonosov also attempted to play a prank which would not have helped any had I not, in my capacity as protector, prevented it. I can say further only that the students did not pass their time here entirely in vain. If in truth Vinogradov, on his part, hardly learned much besides the German language, and if I had to take action on account of him more than any of the others lest he fall into harm and be subjected to academic penalties, on the other hand I cannot but say that Lomonosov made especially good progress in the sciences. I had more frequent opportunity to speak with him than with Reiser, and his manner of reasoning is better known to me. The cause of their debts has been revealed only now, after their departure. They indulged immoderately in dissolute living and were passionately fond of the feminine sex. So long as they were here in person no one dared say anything about them because they held everyone in dread through their threats. Their departure freed me from many cares. When they saw how much money must be paid out because of them, and when they heard what difficulties were experienced in negotiations for the reduction of the creditors' claims, only then did they become penitent; and they not only begged pardon of me for having caused me such anxiety, but declared that they wished to behave entirely differently in the future, and that I would find them entirely changed persons if they were just arriving in Marburg. Throughout this Lomonosov in particular could not say a word, for sorrow and tears."

In Freiberg, where our students arrived on July 25, different arrangements awaited them. The mining councillor, or *Bergrat*, Henckel was already informed in detail and forewarned about their mode of life, and strict orders were given him which he passed on to them forthwith. The yearly maintenance of each student was reduced to 200 rubles. Furthermore, Henckel kept the money himself, paid the accounts, and gave one thaler a month to each student for his own use. Besides, it was announced throughout the whole town that no one should honor the students' debts since the Russian Academy of Sciences had no intention of paying them. At that time there was in Freiberg a professor of elocution from the Academy of Sciences, Junker, who was studying the salt industry under a government commission. He became acquainted with the students and wrote as follows to Baron Korff about the impression they made: "The students, it is true, make a slovenly impression in their dress, but with respect to their studies they have been so taught, both the *Bergrat* and I are convinced, that they have laid an excellent foundation. To us this is clear proof of their diligence in Marburg. Moreover, at the first lectures in the laboratories, which I attended, I could not help noticing their praiseworthy love of knowledge and desire to learn the fundamentals of things."

Here the students finally entered upon the study of metallurgy and mining, for which they had come. But the good relations which existed at first between Lomonosov and Henckel were quickly spoiled, and as a result of a series of unpleasant incidents, in May 1740 Lomonosov left Freiberg. Both of them wrote repeatedly to St. Petersburg about their conflicts. Henckel accused Lomonosov of not wishing to study with him, pointed out his constant disorderly conduct when drunk, complained of his demands for money beyond what was provided by the new instructions, and the like. On his side, Lomonosov thought that the cause of all the trouble lay in Henckel's cupidity, his disagreeable nature, his inability, and his unwillingness to pass on his knowledge. However, during his stay in Freiberg Lomonosov unquestionably became acquainted with mining and with the methods of smelting metals from ore, as is evident from the *Metallurgy* which he wrote two years later.

To this should be added that at the very end of 1739 Lomonosov sent from Freiberg to the Academy of Sciences a regular account of his occupations, a dissertation on a physical subject, and, in addition, an ode written on the occasion of the victory of the Russian army over the Turks at Stavuchany on August 18 of the same year and of the capture of the fortress of Khotin on August 19. It was entitled *Ode to the Sovereign Empress Anna Ioannovna on the Victory over the Turks and Tartars, and on the capture of Khotin, in the year 1739.* It begins with these lines:

> A sudden transport seized the mind,
> And led atop the highest hill,
> Where in the forest ceased the wind;
> In the deep valley all was still.

To the ode was appended a "Letter on the Rules of Russian Poetry"—probably the result of lengthy deliberation. In this letter Lomonosov not only gives the rules of writing verse, but enters upon a polemic against V. K. Tredyakovsky, criticizing his booklet of 1735, *Method of Composing Russian Verses*, which Lomonosov had acquired in 1736 and taken abroad with him. In quality, in the musical nature of its verses, and in meter, Lomonosov's ode surpassed everything Russian poetry had hitherto produced. Consequently it seemed to those who read it absolute perfection. In the Academy of Sciences, Adjunct V. E. Adadurov and Academician Y. Y. Stählin examined the ode. "We were very much surprised," says the latter, "at this meter of verse, which had never before existed in the Russian language . . . all read it, and were amazed at this new meter. . . ."

This ode marked the beginning of Lomonosov's fame as a poet.

From Freiberg, with no money whatever, Lomonosov first set out for the fair at Leipzig in the hope of finding Baron Keyserling, the Russian ambassador and former president of the Academy of Sciences. Lomonosov himself describes his wanderings thus: "Arriving here (in Leipzig) on May 19, I was informed, to my chagrin and unhappiness, that he had gone to Cassel for the forthcoming nuptials of Prince Friedrich. Finding several good friends from Marburg in Leipzig who wanted to take me with them to Cassel, I decided to go there. In Freiberg I not only had nothing to eat, but nothing more to study. I already knew the art of testing, and the chemistry course was finished. Arriving in Cassel, I again had to be informed to my utmost displeasure that nothing was known about our ambassador. In such a hopeless situation, not knowing where Keyserling was, I thought it best to set out for Petersburg through Holland if I could find no refuge with Baron Golovnik (at that time the Russian ambassador to Holland). At first I went to Marburg in order to provide myself with money for the journey from my old friends. I did not dare to be a burden to Wolf, since I had learned from him that he had received the money due him from Petersburg only a few weeks before. Furthermore, I observed that he did not wish to be involved in this matter. Thus, from Marburg I went to Frankfurt and thence by water to Rotterdam and the Hague. The baron refused me any sort of help and did not wish to be implicated in the affair in any way. Thereupon I went to Amsterdam and there found several merchant acquaintances from Archangel, who advised me strongly against returning to Petersburg without orders. They depicted a host of dangers and misfortunes and I therefore had to return again to Germany. The danger and need I suffered en route are horrible even to recall. . . . At the present time I am living incognito in Marburg with friends and am getting practice in algebra, hoping to apply it to theoretical chemistry and physics. I am consoling myself for the time being that I was able to visit famous cities, talk with some skilled chemists, inspect their laboratories, and look at mines in Hessen and Siegen."

What Lomonosov does not mention is his marriage in Marburg on June 6, 1740, to Elizabeth Zilch, the daughter of a church elder whom he had met during his three years as a student there. This marriage remained unknown to everyone for many years.

On his return journey the danger which Lomonosov says he underwent happened in this way. Having crossed the Dutch border into Germany, he arrived one evening at some hamlet or other where he planned to spend the night. In the tavern he found a Prussian officer, a canvasser for recruits. The tall powerful Lomonosov attracted general attention and the officer invited him to have supper with him. During the meal he praised the royal service, got his guest drunk, and persuaded him to enlist. On waking the following morning, Lomonosov found a red necktie around his neck. He was a Prussian royal hussar! Two days later, Lomonosov went to the fortress of Wesel along with other recruits. In order to conceal from the soldiers accompanying him his plan to escape, he pretended to be entirely satisfied with his lot. Nevertheless on arrival he was not lodged in free quarters like the other recruits but in the fortress itself, where he had to sleep in the guardroom. Every evening he lay down to sleep as early as possible so as to have slept his fill when the other soldiers were only dozing off.

Waking one night after midnight, Lomonosov noticed that everyone was sleeping soundly, and quickly put his plan of flight into effect. Climbing the rampart in the darkness, he dropped into the moat unobserved by the watchman, swam across it, scaled another rampart, dropped into a second moat, and swam across. Then he got safely over the palisade and other obstacles and made his way to the open field. From there he had to reach the Westphalian frontier, seven kilometers away, by daybreak. Soon it began to dawn, and a cannon shot thundered from the fortress—his flight had been observed—mounted hussars were riding after him. Exerting all his strength, Lomonosov got to the frontier in time. He slept during the day in a deep forest, and in the evening went on farther, passing himself off as a poor student, and reached Marburg without mishap.

Meanwhile, the Academy of Sciences, learning of Lomonosov's departure from Freiberg, sent him, and in duplicate to Keyserling and Golovnik, order after order to return at once to Petersburg. When a communication was received from Lomonosov at Marburg, the money necessary for the journey was sent him.

In the spring of 1741 he once more set out for Holland, going first to Utrecht and thence to Amsterdam. There the Russian plenipotentiary, the diplomatic agent Oldekop, provided him with good clothes and money and sent him on a sloop to the Russian ambassador, Baron Golovnik, at the Hague. The latter met Lomonosov with more affability on this occasion and within a few days equipped him with everything he needed, gave him money, and sent him back to Amsterdam. After waiting there a short time Lomonosov boarded a ship going to St. Petersburg. Before doing so, however, he wrote to his wife of his safe arrival in Holland and instructed her not to write to him until he informed her of his destination and address. He arrived in Petersburg on July 8, 1741. However, his circumstances during his first years in the academy were such that he decided not to write to his wife. She herself in 1743 turned to Baron Golovnik with the request that he forward a letter to Lomonosov. Golovnik sent her letter to Chancellor Count Bestuzhev at St. Petersburg. He handed it over for delivery to Academician Y. Y. Stählin, who preserved all details of the incident. Lomonosov answered his wife at once and sent her a hundred gold rubles. She went to him under the escort of her brother, Ivan Andreyevich Zilch, and probably arrived in the summer of 1744.

On his return to the academy, Lomonosov was not subjected to any punishment whatsoever for his affairs abroad. J. Schumacher, the director of the chancellery, gave him two rooms in the academy building, on the second line of the Vasilyevsky Ostrov (now No. 45). At first he had to fulfill various chance commissions: the preparation of a catalogue of minerals, translations for the *Petersburg News,* and the composition of an ode (which was then part of an academician's round of duties). Lomonosov's poetic compositions were so distinct in their language from the works of the other poets of the day as to attract general attention at once. After specimens of his learning which he had brought with him, including some of his scholarly dissertations, had been examined (with the closest cooperation of Schumacher) on January 8, 1742, Lomonosov was made an adjunct of the academy in the department of physics at an annual stipend of 360 rubles. It would have been possible to live very well on this amount, owing to the low price level of the time, if only the money had been paid. But at that time the academy was without any funds whatsoever and, instead of a cash stipend, one had to be satisfied with taking books from the academy bookshop at a nominal price and selling them—if buyers could be found.

On November 25, 1741, a court revolution brought the daughter of Peter I, Elizabeth Petrovna, to the throne. The decade of rule by Baltic Germans headed by Biron was at an end, and the hostile feeling against them, long held in check, found free expression. The Academy of Sciences was not unaffected by this since it was made up almost exclusively of foreigners, and all those who had suffered under

the domination of Schumacher, the all-powerful director
of the chancellery, hastened to take advantage of the op-
portunities which had arisen. Denunciations and accusations against him poured into the senate. The affair ended
with Schumacher's arrest in October 1742 and the appointment of a committee of investigation. To this period belongs a series of noisy quarrels between Lomonosov and
Germans living in the same house with him, the gardener
of the academy, and his friends. As a result of these quarrels
Lomonosov received some severe wounds, was arrested, and
taken to the police station and to the chancery of the chief
of police. Several law suits charging assault and slander
were brought against him, but they were not tried during
his lifetime and were still pending in the 1780's when
Lomonosov had long been dead.

At that same time, previous to April 1743, complaints
were also made by the academicians against Lomonosov.
Accusations before an examining committee included dis-
courteous behavior toward members of the academy, in-
terrupting sessions of the academic conference by indecent
pranks, and rowdy conduct in the department of geography.
He paid no attention to the summons of the investigating
committee until he was arrested on May 28, 1743. He remained under domiciliary arrest until January 18, 1744,
when a ukase was issued: "To free Adjunct Lomonosov
from punishment since he has learnt his lesson; but for the
offenses which he had committed, that he should beg pardon of the professors; and because he had committed such
misdemeanors in the commission and conference, as well as
in the courtroom, to give him, Lomonosov, only half a year's
salary according to his present stipend; to announce this to
him in the chancery of the ruling senate with the postscript
that if he subsequently is found in such misdemeanors he
will be punished and denied appeal."

All this was fulfilled; the pardon was announced publicly in a session of the conference of the academy. A text in Lomonosov's own hand, in Latin, was recently found in the archives of the Academy of Sciences. Here is a translation of it:

"I, Mikhailo Lomonosov, before the assembly of the academy, do publicly and sincerely declare that I can not and do not wish to infringe on the good name or reputation of the most noted gentlemen, professors of this Imperial Academy of Sciences. In addition I declare that I abhor from the depths of my soul, solemnly recant, and would like to consider unsaid those abusive words, unreasonable in the highest degree, with which I being drunk slandered the gentlemen professors on the twenty-sixth day of the month of April of the past year, 1743. I most humbly beg and implore of the noted academicians present, and also of those absent, that they forgive me with benevolence. I realize the monstrous bounds of my unforgivable error and promise to mend my ways in the most honorable fashion. This entreaty, pronounced publicly by me on the twenty-seventh day of the month of January, 1744, Mikhailo Lomonosov verifies by the signature of his own hand."

After this event Lomonosov did not permit himself further misdemeanors of this sort.

The chief cause of his unhappy relationships as an adjunct with the academicians seems to have been that he sensed his superiority over the majority of them. He felt that he was able to perform great things in science, but that conditions were unfavorable for this.

In accordance with an imperial command Lomonosov's salary was restored to its original amount after six months. Schumacher, on his part, having emerged from this affair cleared and in the right, was reinstated in his position. His accusers were sentenced to punishment by flogging, and one even to the death penalty. However, all were pardoned by order of Elizabeth.

Such were the chief events of the first year of Lomonosov's academic life. Naturally, he was busy not only with the matters just described but also with his regular duties. He taught one of the students of the university chemistry, mineralogy, style, and poetry in the Russian language. During this period several of his literary works appeared, including his setting of the psalms, *The Morning and Evening Meditations on the Divine Majesty*. These, perhaps the best of his poetic works, were written while he was under arrest. In them is expressed the sincere emotion of the naturalist as he stands in the presence of the majestic phenomena of nature. Consider the beauty of the verses from the *Morning Meditations* devoted to a description of the activity of the sun:

Oh, if a mortal's power could stretch so high—
If mortal sight could reach that glorious sun,
And look undazzled at its majesty,
'Twould seem a fiery ocean burning on
From time's first birth, whose ever-flaming ray
Could ne'er extinguish'd be by time's decay.

There waves of fire 'gainst waves of fire are dashing,
And know no bounds; there hurricanes of flame,
As if in everlasting combat flashing,
Roar with a fury which no time can tame:
There molten mountains boil like ocean-waves,
And rain in burning streams the welkin laves.

Bowring, *Specimens of the Russian Poets.*

One can believe that Lomonosov had himself seen everything that is described here, although these phenomena were not observable until the last quarter of the nineteenth century. Also very beautiful is the beginning of the *Evening Meditations*:

On Seeing the Aurora Borealis

The day retires, the mists of night are spread
Slowly o'er nature, darkening as they rise:
The gloomy clouds are gathering round our head,
And twilight's latest glimmering gently dies:
The stars awake in heaven's abyss of blue:
Say, who can count them?—who can sound it?—who?

Even as a sand in the majestic sea,
A diamond-atom on a hill of snow,
A spark amidst a Hecla's majesty,
An unseen mote where maddened whirlwinds blow,
Am I midst scenes like these—the mighty thought
O'erwhelms me—I am nought, or less than nought.

Bowring, *Specimens of the Russian Poets.*

In addition Lomonosov composed several eulogistic odes
to ruling personages which found much favor at court. Composing odes as well as arranging pyrotechnic displays was
one of the academician's duties. On the scientific side he
wrote at that time a book on metallurgy and prepared a
series of scientific dissertations (which will be examined
later) chiefly concerned with physics. But his scientific activity was most manifest after his appointment as professor
—that is, as academician—to the chair of chemistry.

The chair of chemistry in the Russian Academy of Sciences had, from the very founding of the academy, been
more or less neglected. The first academician to occupy it
was the Courlander M. Burger, who arrived in St. Petersburg in March 1726. On the twenty-second of July in the
same year, as he was returning in a drunken state from the
house of his friend, Academician Blumentrost, he fell out
of his carriage and was fatally injured.[3] Shortly afterward

---

[3] This incident, by the way, depicts the manners in general of
the academy of that time. Drunkenness was equally widespread
among Russians and Germans.

the well-known naturalist J. G. Gmelin was invited to take his place. Although he possessed no special chemical knowledge, he was a good botanist. On that account he participated in the expedition which in 1732 set out to explore Siberia. He remained there ten years, until 1743. On his return to St. Petersburg his time was occupied exclusively with work on his valuable collection of plants. Soon he was back in Germany, having given up the chair of chemistry. Obviously neither of these academicians did anything for the department, and in an academy which had all other kinds of scientific workrooms and laboratories, there was not that indispensable tool of the chemist—a chemical laboratory.

Since he had special knowledge of chemistry, Lomonosov had always counted on filling that chair in the academy. In fact, it was promised to him even before the students were sent abroad. In 1745 he took advantage of the return of the court to St. Petersburg to submit a petition to Elizabeth that he be made professor of chemistry. In it he referred in detail both to the labors by which he had acquired the necessary knowledge and to his dissertations. The petition was first examined by the academic assembly, which ordered Lomonosov to write a dissertation on metallurgy. He fulfilled the task in all haste, the dissertation was approved, and the academy presented Lomonosov to the senate for appointment as professor. The ukase on his promotion was published on July 25, 1745, and from that time on Lomonosov was a full member of the academy. On August 12 he took part for the first time in a session of the conference.

Lomonosov's economic situation became much better as a professor and academician. His salary mounted to 660 rubles a year but, as far as we can see by such documents as have been preserved, he almost never had any money. We find constant requests for the payment of his salary in advance, lawsuits on bills, and so on. In his capacity as security for Academician Gmelin, who had gone abroad and did not return to St. Petersburg, Lomonosov in 1748 had to pay more than his yearly income, 715 rubles. It was only considerably later that Gmelin returned this money.

Just at this time Lomonosov's wife arrived from Marburg, and he received a large professor's apartment in the same house where he had lived previously. Thus he was in general more comfortably settled than he had ever been before. A peaceful life brought even more capacity for work. In these years of the exact sciences he worked for the most part at physics. In 1746 he published his own translation of Wolf's *Experimental Physics*, which is interesting from diverse points of view. In the preface he explained in detail that recent progress in the natural sciences was the result of scholars having abandoned Aristotelian philosophy and begun to apply the experimental method, which required that every hypothesis be tested by experiment. In consequence physics was taught exclusively with the aid of experiments, from which theories were formulated. "Moreover," he writes, "I was obliged to select words for use as names of various physical instruments, operations, and natural objects. Although these may at first seem somewhat strange, I hope that through use they will in time become better known." This translation, therefore, contains the groundwork of Russian scientific language, of which Lomonosov was the creator. In fact we now use and are quite at home with many terms then introduced by him.

Of very great significance was Lomonosov's effort to propagate education as widely as possible throughout Russia. He proposed and brought about the adoption of a practice never before suggested whereby, as the first of Russian professors to do so, he began to give public lectures on physics. In the *St. Petersburg News* of 1746 appeared this description, written by chroniclers of the time, of the first lecture: "This twentieth of June, by order of the president of the Academy of Sciences, the Actual Chamberlain of Her Imperial Majesty and Knight of the Order of St. Anna, His Excellency Kirill Grigoryevich Razumovsky, Professor Lomonosov of the same academy began to give public lectures on experimental physics in the Russian language. On this occasion, in addition to a numerous group of military and civil officials of various ranks, the president of the academy himself was present with several gentlemen of the court and other personages of importance. On account of the holiday today the second lecture is postponed until the coming Thursday, but from then on they will be held on Tuesdays and Fridays from three to five o'clock in the afternoon." The lectures ceased soon after the departure of the president, the seventy-year-old Razumovsky, and on August 5 we find the following information in the same *News*: "Enthusiasts in experimental physics are hereby informed that the professor of the Academy of Sciences, Mr. Lomonosov, will resume his public lectures next Friday at the hours formerly announced, from three to five." Whether many enthusiasts went to hear these lectures, and how long they continued, is not known.

I shall say more later about his other works in physics, especially several dissertations, since they are important in the history of the development of physics. In the meantime, Lomonosov did not give up his other occupations. He continued to compose literary works and, among other things, in 1748 wrote an ode to celebrate Elizabeth's accession to the throne, for which he received 2,000 rubles. In the same year he published *A Short Guide to Eloquence,* which was long considered authoritative.

Having been made a professor, Lomonosov was in a position to bring about the building of a chemical laboratory at the Academy of Sciences. For the promotion of this project he brought to bear all of his perseverance and ability in order to overcome the many opposing forces and achieve his goal. When he had just been appointed as adjunct, he submitted to the academy a petition for the building of a laboratory, without which, then even as now, experimental work in chemistry was inconceivable. He renewed this petition almost every year, but always without success. After Schumacher's restoration to authority, the previous good relations between them naturally were spoiled, and all requests received the same answer—no money. The petition, submitted in 1745, was reasoned out in great detail, with a description and plan of a laboratory appended to it. Many academicians supported this petition, which was sent to the senate. This time the project took a better turn. On the first of July there followed a signed ukase for the construction of a laboratory at the expense of "Her Majesty's cabinet." But the matter was so delayed by certain stipulations (in Lomonosov's opinion, all through Schumacher, the director of affairs of the chancellery) that not until 1748, after numerous reminders, were negotiations for the construction announced. Then in the autumn the laboratory was built, under Lomonosov's supervision, by the contractor Gorbunov at a cost of 1,344 rubles.

The laboratory was located in the botanical garden of the academy, a few steps from the house where Lomonosov lived, between the first and second lines of the Vasilyevsky Ostrov, behind Central Avenue, in what is now No. 45 on the second line and No. 52 on the first. It was a stone structure supported by vaults of very small dimensions in comparison with present-day chemical laboratories: 14 meters (6½ sazhen) long, 10½ meters (5 sazhen) wide, and 5 meters (7 arshin) high. In the interior were three rooms. Just opposite the entrance was a large square room in the center of which was set up a hearth—that is, a foundation upon which chemical furnaces might be set up—and a wide flue. Then there were two small rooms; in one, the larger, lectures were delivered to the students, the chemical balances were placed, and the results of experiments were written up. In the other smaller room was a storage closet for chemical utensils and materials. The equipment of the laboratory was designed by Lomonosov himself and met the demands of the time. Detailed notes were kept of everything that was acquired. In 1749 a new office of "laboratorian" was created at the laboratory: that official had to be a man "who is able to handle fire." This was the first chemical laboratory in Russia to serve the purpose of instruction and the pursuit of chemical research, just as Mikhail Vasilyevich Lomonosov was the first Russian chemist.

It should be added that Lomonosov's chemical laboratory was destroyed in 1783, after which the entire site of the academy was given over to the newly founded Imperial Russian Academy, which erected buildings with the façade on the first line (No. 52), where they stand even now. After the merger of the Russian Academy with the Academy of Sciences in 1841, the Roman Catholic Theological Academy took over the building. Now the Leningrad District Pedagogical School of the People's Commissariat of Education occupies the spot.

CHAPTER 3

Lomonosov's work in physics—The corpuscular philosophy—His atomic theory and The Elements of Mathematical Chemistry—Particles and atoms—Reflections on the Cause of Heat and Cold—Mechanical theory of heat—The principle of the conservation of energy—Experiment on the theory of the elastic force of air and the supplement thereto—The kinetics of gases—The theory of the diffusion of light—Discourse on solids and liquids—The freezing of mercury—The thermometers of Fahrenheit, Réaumur, Delisle, Celsius, and Lomonosov.

THE building of the chemical laboratory marks the end of the first period of Lomonosov's work, and I think it necessary to survey that period at this point, the more so because he himself counted it the most important side of his activity. "Poetry is my solace —physics, my profession," he says in his *Grammar* (1755). In Chapter 2 we have already seen how the writings of Robert Boyle contributed to the basic theme of his scientific investigations, which consisted of, first, the study of those minute particles ("insensible," as Lomonosov called them) or corpuscles of which all bodies are composed, through the agency of chemistry, physics, and mathematics, and, second, an explanation of the scientific facts of physics and chemistry with the aid of the properties of the corpuscles.

At first Lomonosov planned to write a great work which would unite all the sciences mentioned by applying the corpuscular theory. Several times during his life he made a great effort to write such a "corpuscular theory," as he calls it in one of his letters to Euler. But always some cause or other forced him to stop at the very beginning, when he had hardly sketched out the plan of the work. However, the separate chapters of this great undertaking are almost all before us: those dissertations, discourses, and treatises which he delivered to the public, chiefly in the formal sessions of the academy.

Lomonosov made lengthy preparations for every oration or discourse of this kind. He always began with a collection of quotations from various authors who had said something on the subject of a given concrete theme. Then he noted down his own opinions, propositions, and questions, and made a draft of the plans for work. Among his papers several collections of notes of this kind, carefully numbered, have been preserved. Then he arranged these notes in a definite order, quoted citations from various authors when necessary, and afterward expounded his views in writing. Generally speaking, his notebooks contain few erasures; obviously his work was already composed in his head, so that it required only notation on paper. The Latin in which he wrote his scientific works (only a few are written in Russian) is excellent. Its distinguishing characteristics are precision and keenness of expression, beautiful style, brevity, and expressiveness. In the main, he used Russian for the "orations" and reports given in public gatherings. Here, too, we find expressive euphonious turns of speech which sometimes, especially in the eulogistic orations, seem bombastic and unnatural today.

As has been shown, the basic idea mentioned above combined his scientific works, especially those on physics and chemistry, into one harmonious whole. For a convenient survey we shall divide Lomonosov's scientific work into three periods. The first, which lasts until the building of the chemical laboratory, may be called the physics period, since he devoted most of this time to work in the most important departments of physics, on the basis of the corpuscular theory. The second period, from the construction of the laboratory until his own house was built in 1757, was occupied principally with chemistry. Finally, the third period, from 1757 until his death (April 4, 1765) was devoted to various applied sciences—navigation, geography, meteorology, astronomy, regional studies, metallurgy and mining, mineralogy, geology, and others. In 1757 Lomonosov also assumed various administrative duties in the Academy of Sciences.

In this chapter we shall dwell on Lomonosov's important works in the field of physics, as component parts of the great corpuscular philosophy. In order to give a more unified impression, however, several works which were written during later periods of his life will be included. Far from everything he wrote was published, but there have been preserved among his papers rough drafts of those chapters which never saw the light of day. These drafts and notebooks were first sorted out by me in 1902 and 1903, and published in an abridged Russian translation in 1904 in my study, *Lomonosov as a Physical Chemist*. Full translations of them may be found in my book, *The Works of M. V. Lomonosov in Physics and Chemistry*, which has just been published (edition of Academy of Sciences, 1936).

Before discussing this material (the writings of Lomonosov), what was said in Chapter 2 about the fundamental propositions of physics in the first half of the eighteenth century should be amplified briefly. As true investigators of nature, making use of the inductive method of investigation, the physicists set experimentation above everything else. From the results of experiments and observations they formulated basic laws; to explain those laws they constructed propositions or hypotheses. These in turn were subjected to verification through experimentation. The hypotheses of that time, in general, were uniform and from the modern point of view quite incomplete. Almost everything was explained by mysterious delicate fluids—the matter of heat, light, gravity, electricity, and so on—which were invisible and indistinguishable. Truth compels us to say that imponderable fluids of this kind continued to be used (for electricity) almost to the last quarter of the past century.

The fundamental question of the composition of matter was decided then as now on the assumption that matter cannot be divided indefinitely, but only up to a certain limit. The atom, which is incapable of further division, is such a limit. This proposition harks back to remotest antiquity, and even Greek and Roman philosophers believed that all visible and perceptible substances were composed of atoms. This in substance was the opinion in the beginning of the eighteenth century. Physicists conceived of the atoms as having varied forms, and only very few took the trouble to investigate the properties of these elementary particles of matter owing to the utter lack of means for investigating atoms through experimentation at the time. Today the view of the essential nature of matter remains the same, but with the enormous difference that the existence of atoms is now not hypothesis but precisely proved fact. Today atoms are not so much studied as the still smaller parts of which they are composed.

In Lomonosov's day, just as now, it was self-evident that, if the complex composition of all substances from atoms was admitted, then the logically inevitable conclusion was that all physical phenomena, all properties and qualities of substances, depend exclusively on the properties of these atoms. Therefore the investigation of the properties of atoms or, in general, of the elementary particles which go to make up substances must lead to an "explanation" of the properties of these substances also—in other words, to a clarification of the causal dependence between the one and the other. Of course all this was fully recognized by the philosophers of the eighteenth century, but it was considered so self-evident that it was rarely mentioned at all.

Lomonosov, who always penetrated to the very kernel of a problem, understood clearly the full importance of the exact investigation of the elementary particles of substances. As he expresses himself in one of his works: "To search for the causes of visible properties which occur on the surface of substances in their internal composition—that is the final goal of research." He did not suspect how difficult this task was. The unknown often seems immensely simpler to us than it is in actuality. Only now, almost two centuries later, are we just beginning to make estimates in this field, and then only after we have discovered the complex structure of the atoms themselves and the necessity of studying their component parts—electrons and the positive nuclei of atoms. At the present time scientists are confident that in the comparatively near future the goal which Lomonosov set may be attained.

The foundation of all that Lomonosov performed lies, of course, in the hypothesis that substances are constructed from elementary particles and the properties of those particles make it possible to explain the properties of the substances which they form. According to his view, each physical body consists of extremely small bodies of matter which cannot be further subdivided physically and which are capable of mutual cohesion. In his terminology they are insensible physical particles—"insensible" meaning that it is impossible to see them directly with the help of any kind of microscope or other device. The properties of substances, first of all their state of aggregation—that is, whether they are gaseous, liquid, or solid—are conditioned by the properties of these particles. Also, different properties of bodies are a result only of differences in the elementary particles themselves or of the way they are bound together.

Lomonosov stresses especially that each such insensible particle represents a substance—that is, it has certain definite, even though very minute, dimensions, possesses mass and, in general, all the attributes of bodies accessible to our senses. Like all physical bodies, elementary particles are able to move in accordance with the laws of motion taught by mechanics, while without motion they cannot collide with one another, push each other, or in any other way act upon each other or undergo change. All bodies have the qualities of particles, such as color, taste, smell, and the like, by which they are differentiated. Such properties of all bodies, like heat and cold and weight, reciprocal cohesion of the parts of the body, change in exactly the same ways as a result of the union, division, or transfer of the insensible particles, so that an adequate cause of the qualities of the particles consists in their dimensions, external appearance, and movements. Furthermore, since the dimensions, form, and movements of bodies are recognized and characterized by the aid of mathematics and mechanics, the laws of these sciences applied to the insensible physical particles of bodies make it possible to understand the origin of the "particular" qualities of substances. With regard to the form of the elementary particles, Lomonosov held them to be spherical in shape, very hard, with insignificant roughness, and not subject to any kind of physical change.

Bodies which differ from each other chemically also possess different particles which differ in their chemical composition. It is found in chemical analysis that an infinitely great number of component parts is never obtained but, rather, comparatively few that are incapable of being further broken down chemically. These are "the fundaments" in Lomonosov's terminology, or what we now call the chemical elements. Each elementary particle of a compound substance contains elements in itself in exactly the same proportions as the whole compound substance. In that fact lies the cause of the chemical differentiation of substances.

Thus the elementary particles of a compound substance,

or corpuscles, are made up of "elements" which correspond fully to the contemporary conception of the molecule as made up of atoms. Finally, the corpuscles may be heterogeneous if the same elements which form them are combined in a different way. Heterogeneous corpuscles produce heterogeneous substances, which are made up of the same elements but not combined in the same way and therefore not possessing the same properties. From all this follows the necessity for the chemist, as well as the physicist, to know mathematics and mechanics in order to investigate the phenomena produced by the movements of the insensible physical particles.

These first dissertations of Lomonosov, which I have just quoted in brief, bear the titles, *Of the Insensible Physical Particles which Compose Natural Substances, and in which is the Adequate Source of the Properties of Particles* and *The Elements of Mathematical Chemistry.* In these treatises there is clearly visible on the one hand the tremendous influence exercised on Lomonosov by his acquaintance with the natural philosophers of the seventeenth and eighteenth centuries, and—most of all—with the mathematical philosophy of Christian Wolf. This enabled him to develop and expound his ideas, which were original, in strict logical sequence. Lomonosov's views, which closely resembled those that did not find expression until as recently as the end of the nineteenth century, were more than a hundred years before their time. His method of exposition, however, achieved complete clarity and precision through the use of the mathematical method which he borrowed from Christian Wolf.

I consider the circumstance especially interesting that, in speaking of the elementary particles of substances, Lomonosov distinguishes two types: the smaller ones, which he calls elements, and the larger ones, composed of elements, which he calls corpuscles. This distinction is the basis of the whole orderly structure of contemporary chemistry. Today we call corpuscles "molecules" and differentiate them strictly from atoms, of which, in their turn, all molecules are composed. An essentially clear understanding of the chemical particle (molecule) as a combination of a precise number of uniform or dissimilar atoms has been for seventy years the conception on which all chemistry rests. History shows that the development of modern and most recent chemistry became possible only after the international congress of chemists at Karlsruhe in 1860, where exact conceptions of the molecule and the atom were formulated. (The congress was summoned for this purpose.) But Lomonosov's labors played no part in the development of these propositions since all of the dissertations mentioned remained unpublished during his lifetime. They were first published in my translation only in 1904.

There is no room for doubt that Lomonosov's hypothesis concerning the construction of all substances from atoms, viewed as material corporeal particles, occupies a high position among the atomic hypotheses of the first half of the eighteenth century. And, if it had been published in connection with all its further developments, it might possibly have had a great influence on the evolution of physics and chemistry. With further regard to this hypothesis, it may be noted that Lomonosov, like the other philosophers of his time (although he considered his atoms to be "insensible" particles, that is, not accessible to observation) still undoubtedly conceived of them as much larger than they actually seem to be according to the latest researches.

Lomonosov continued to develop in various directions his hypothesis concerning the connection between the properties of atoms, physical properties, and all the phenomena of physics. From 1744 to 1748 he worked with special intensity. Dating from this period we have a series of interesting works by him which deal in general with the most important physical properties of substances, and chiefly with thermal phenomena and the gaseous state. Throughout his life he returned repeatedly to this subject and left us in addition his views on the nature of light and extensive researches on electricity. Some of these writings were published during his life and some preserved in manuscript. All of them are closely connected with the basic hypothesis of the structure of matter, and throughout them all one necessary consequence of his atomic conception runs like a scarlet thread. It is this: since all properties of substances depend exclusively on the properties and movements of the elementary particles of which they are composed and can be fully explained by the purely mechanical difference in the motion of these particles, then, evidently, those delicate "matters" of fire, light, elasticity, electricity, and other fluids, which at that time explained the properties of heat, light, and other physical phenomena (as we saw in the physics of Christian Wolf) are rendered absolutely unnecessary. And indeed, in this respect Lomonosov was no follower of Wolf or other prominent physicists of his time, but utterly dispensed with any kind of auxiliary mysterious substances. This absorbing fact, which shows the originality of Lomonosov's ideas, brings his views close to those of modern times.

Let us now examine his dissertation, *Reflections on the Cause of Heat and Cold*, written in 1744 and printed three years later. It is evident in studying the phenomena of the heating of bodies that the sufficient cause of heat lies in motion—but the motion of the substance itself does not heat it. Consequently heating may be caused only by internal motion, that is, by the movement of insensible particles of a substance, particles which move with the help of a threefold kind of motion: progressive when they change places with regard to each other; vibrative when they waver back and forth; and rotatory when they rotate on their axes.

Applying this principle to the particles of solids, it is evident that they can only rotate, for their stable interconnection prevents them from progressive or vibrative motion. Therefore rotary motion, since the particles of either solid, liquid, or gaseous substances are capable of it, must be considered the cause of heat.

All phenomena arising through heat (for instance, transfer of heat from one body to another) can be explained by rotary motion. The melting of solid substances is explained by the fact that during the heating process their particles begin to rotate with increasing speed; consequently, having roughnesses on their surface, they collide with each other all the more strongly. At first, therefore, the hardness of the substance diminishes, then it melts, and finally, under even greater heat, the particles lose their interconnection completely and the substance can exist only in the form of vapor.

In the same way liquid substances, and gaseous substances even more, always have a heating rotary motion of the elementary particles of which they are composed. We cannot conceive of the greatest possible speed of movement and therefore cannot say what would be the greatest possible degree of heat. On the other hand, we can easily conceive of a complete cessation of the movements of the particles, which would be the condition producing the greatest possible cold. This we cannot obtain on earth because liquids are known to us which do not freeze under the greatest cold—that is, they still possess a heating movement of the particles.

Having thus established the nature of heat as the motion of the particles of a body, Lomonosov went on to an examination of the opinions of contemporary philosophers on the subject of the "matter" of fire (*teplorod*). Such a substance cannot exist; for instance, whence does this "substance of fire" come when gunpowder ignites from a small

spark in severe cold? Neither does the expansion of substances under heat explain its existence, for different substances expand at different rates when heated the same
number of degrees. The philosophers prove the existence
of this substance of fire by the fact that a metal like lead increases in weight when roasted. But the slag thus obtained,
heated red-hot with coal at an even higher temperature,
gives metal back again. When thoroughly heated, metal is
always surrounded by air, and undoubtedly the increase in
weight results from the union of the metal with particles of
air. Heat also may be transmitted over a distance through
the agency of the ether, which fills the entire space of the
universe, for it receives the heating motion and transmits it
to other bodies—for instance, from the sun to the earth.

Since it properly concerns the chemical phase of his
activity, I shall say more in Chapter 5 about Lomonosov's
opinions developed in this dissertation on the nature of fire
and of the phenomena which result when metals are
heated in air. The mechanical theory of heat just quoted
above, which negates and proves the impossibility of the
existence of a "matter" of heat or fire, was more than a
century before its time. This is essentially a theory of
modern times, related to those processes which take place
in substances when subjected to heat. Today, too, we do not
doubt that temperature cannot drop lower than "absolute
zero," where all motion of the particles has ceased. And
about higher temperatures we can only say that no maximum limit can be set for them. Temperatures are now
observed in the stars which are measured at tens of thousands, even millions, of degrees, temperatures absolutely
unobtainable on earth. We can see in the history of physics
that the concept of heat as a type of motion did not become
general among scholars until the 1870's, in spite of the fact
that the classical experiments which proved this proposition
had been published much earlier.

Of these we mention the experiments of Rumford (1798-1799). They consisted of the following two observations. First, while boring metal cylinders such as were then used to make bronze cannon, the production of a very great amount of heat was noted. If, in carrying on this boring process, both metal and drill are immersed in a bath of water, then during the boring the water becomes heated to the boiling point very quickly regardless of its great quantity. This can only be explained by the fact that the mechanical work of boring is converted into heat, that is, that heat consists of some sort of motion. Secondly, in weighing three bottles filled with water, spirits, and mercury under different temperatures, Rumford found that the weight of each was exactly the same in different temperatures both above zero and below, where water turned to ice and gave off a latent warmth while melting. From this the conclusion was drawn that the "matter of fire," the notion of which was then widespread, could play no part in the heating and chilling of liquids in bottles, for in that case the weight of the liquids would have to change. At that very time (1799) the well-known English chemist and physicist Davy published his observations, in which he found that ice melted at a temperature below zero when friction occured betweeen one piece of ice and another. Water formed in this way has a much higher temperature than the surrounding medium. By this Davy was able to prove that heat produced by friction is not borrowed from the surrounding medium. Thus he too came to the conclusion that heat is a form of motion.

However, these proofs of the transformation of mechanical work into heat neither convinced contemporaries nor led them to see the necessity of giving up the "matter of fire," a belief which continued to exist for more than fifty years. It was abandoned only after the work of three scholars, Robert Mayer, Koldring, and Joule, who about

1842 proved conclusively that heat is formed as a result of mechanical work. Especially explicit and detailed were Joule's researches establishing exactly the quantity of heat obtained from a given quantity of work—the so-called "mechanical equivalent of heat." Only from this time did the conception of heat as the movement of the particles of substance begin little by little to be disseminated. But several decades of work by such scholars as Clausius and Hirn were necessary before the "matter of fire" was finally buried. In science old ideas often die thus obstinately, even when their uselessness and falseness have long been quite apparent.

We also find a clear description by Lomonosov of the transformation of work into heat, in which he was guided by the principle of the conservation of energy expressed some years previously (1738) by Daniel Bernoulli, the talented member of the Petersburg Academy of Sciences. By this principle Lomonosov explains the development of heat from friction and from the transfer of heat from a hot substance to a cold one by their mutual contact. This principle, too, began to be disseminated among scholars after the work of Mayer, Koldring, and Joule mentioned above.

A second exceedingly important consequence of Lomonosov's theory of insensible particles was his interesting researches on the structure of gaseous substances in connection with the elastic force of air (1748-1749). Here is the essence of these researches, entitled *Experiment on the Theory of the Elastic Force of Air* and a *Supplement* to this theory.

The elastic force of air (the only gas known at that time) is what Lomonosov calls the capacity of air to expand under diminished pressure and to contract under increased pressure. This capacity is brought about by the tendency of the insensible particles to separate from one another when the pressure is diminished. The air particles—we may call them atoms—are conceived as being very hard, elastic, and spherical in form, with infinitely small irregularities. Experiment shows that air may be compressed to one-thirtieth of its volume under ordinary pressure, that is, its atoms are set far apart. But contact between them is absolutely necessary if the atoms are to act upon each other. These two contradictory but inevitable conclusions can only be reconciled by assuming that not all atoms are to be found in like condition at a given moment. Moreover the condition of individual atoms remains constant for a very short time. Indeed, some atoms are colliding with others at great speed, while some are at the very same moment repelling each other and running into others nearest them—in a word, the atoms are striving to disperse in all directions and to avoid frequent encounters with each other.

The atoms of air possess a certain definite mass and are subject to the force of gravity, due to which the upper ones fall on those under them and push away from them. But in view of the huge number of atoms in the air, it is impossible for each to fall directly on the uppermost point of the one underneath and bound off vertically upward. That would happen only rarely. Most often they would fall on some other point of the lower atoms and be repelled along diagonal lines in accordance with the laws of mechanics. Thus the elasticity would be manifested in all directions. The higher we rise from the earth's surface, the fewer the atoms of the air, until a height is reached where the force of gravity will overcome the force acquired by the descending atoms as they are repelled by those lying underneath them. This will be the upper limit of the earth's atmosphere. Furthermore, the warmer the air, the greater will be the rotary movement of the atoms, the more strongly will they repel one another, and the greater will be the elasticity of the air. And since the maximum possible cold cannot exist on our earth, the atoms of air are always in motion and the air always possesses elastic force, even in the greatest cold observed on earth.

Lomonosov wrote the *Supplement* to his theory of the elastic force of air on the basis of Bernoulli's experiments, which were made in order to determine the height to which a ball would rise when shot out of a vertically placed cannon. From his experiments Bernoulli came to the conclusion that air subjected to very great pressure does not contract in direct proportion to the pressure. Lomonosov pointed out that, according to his theory, this was to be expected because the air atoms, as particles of matter, possess certain extension and volume; under great pressures, therefore, their collisions will take place more frequently than would be called for by the simple ratio between pressure and volume.

The picture of the condition of the particles in the air which Lomonosov presented so exactly down to the least detail does not differ from the contemporary "kinetic theory of gases," as explained in every textbook of physics. Lomonosov had predecessors who proclaimed the ideas fundamental to his theory, but did not develop them. He, on the other hand, developed a finished theory, which is completely analogous to that of the present day.

Ten years previously, in 1738, Daniel Bernoulli published his great work *Hydrodynamics*, written in Latin, which was devoted to researches he had made in St. Petersburg when a member of the academy. These researches deal with the laws of the movement of inelastic fluids, which we now call liquids, and elastic or, as they are now called, gaseous substances. Bernoulli begins the tenth book of his work devoted to the latter by advancing a theory of their structure which makes possible an explanation of the chief properties of elastic fluids: that is, their ponderability, their ability to expand in all directions, and to contract further under increasing pressure. This theory consists in the assumption that an elastic fluid contains small corpuscles which move about with tremendous speed, and, as they strike against the walls of the vessel which contains them, they maintain a pressure inside this vessel. When such a fluid is compressed the number of corpuscles in a unit of volume becomes greater, they strike more frequently against the walls, and the pressure increases. Then from this basic proposition, without developing it at all, Bernoulli evolves the mathematical laws of the movements of elastic fluids. Throughout all this he says nothing about how or by what means the particles of air get into motion.

In the same year, 1738, the Paris Academy of Sciences offered a prize on the question of the nature of fire. Among the many scholars who submitted compositions on this subject was the famous philosopher Voltaire, at that time (although this is little known) a physicist well above the average who had worked a great deal on the problems investigated by contemporary physicists. In his dissertation (which did not receive a prize, although it stood higher in many respects than those which did) he advanced in passing, among other things the idea that air is a collection of small elastic spheres which rebound from each other and in that way exercise pressure on all obstacles which come in their way. These spheres are brought into motion by the "matter" of fire. "If air were completely deprived of fire matter, it would be entirely motionless and inactive," concludes Voltaire.

Undoubtedly Lomonosov was acquainted with Bernoulli's work, and it is quite possible that he also came upon Voltaire's treatise on the nature of fire in the memoirs of the French Academy of Sciences. He was also unquestionably acquainted with Sir Isaac Newton's works devoted to the subject of air.

The theory which Lomonosov evolved represents the development of those basic mutually complementary theses advanced by Bernoulli and Voltaire plus the logical development of Lomonosov's own hypothesis of the elementary particles of substances. Although Lomonosov's dissertation found place in the *Commentaries* of the Academy of Sciences in Latin, it attracted little attention from his contemporaries and is not mentioned by later scholars.

The kinetic theory of gases, as far as we know, was stated anew in 1821 by the Englishman A. Herapath, but no one paid any attention to it. Evidently the time was not yet ripe; the general level of knowledge was still too low for its acceptance. It was the same in 1845 when another Englishman, Waterson, expounded it in detail in an article which he submitted to the Royal Society of London. The decision was that the work did not merit publication, and it fell into the archives of the society, where it was discovered by the physicist Lord Rayleigh, who published it in 1892. At that time the kinetic theory of gases was advanced quite independently by the German physicists Kroenig (1856) and Clausius (1857), and was later elaborated by Maxwell and Boltzmann; thereafter it received general dissemination. D. Bernoulli was "discovered" in 1859, and the passage in his *Hydrodynamics* where elastic fluids are discussed was reproduced. I have never happened to see any reference to Voltaire's ideas on the nature of air, but evidently it fell to me to resurrect Lomonosov's theory in 1904.

Lomonosov's *Supplement* to the theory of the elasticity of air is interesting at the present time only for its explanation of how the volume occupied by a gas fails to conform to the pressure when it is great. First and foremost we must note that the fact itself, which Lomonosov explained after borrowing it from Bernoulli's experiments, had been by no means proven by these experiments. Bernoulli thought that highly compressed air was formed by the combustion of the gunpowder in the gun and thus did not take into account the high temperature developed by the explosion, which was responsible to a significant degree for the increase of pressure in the gases from the powder. Only in the middle of the nineteenth century did exact measurements of the volume of a compressed gas under increase of pressure show that this volume is greater than when calculated on the basis of Boyle's law, which assumes a simple inverse proportionality between the two quantities. Lomonosov's explanation that the real volume, under great pressure, is greater than the calculated volume because the particles of air themselves have a definite extension and occupy some volume, however small, is absolutely correct. An explanation of this fact, essentially identical with Lomonosov's conclusion, was given soon after the appearance of the kinetic theory of gases, in 1864, by the Frenchman Dupré. Later it was elaborated in detail by the Dutch physicist Van der Waals in 1873. In the case cited Lomonosov was 115 years ahead of his time.

In order not to have to return later to the most important works of Lomonosov in the realm of physics, I shall discuss here some of his dissertations of a later period. These are characterized by the same tokens we have just observed; throughout Lomonosov renounced the concept of those delicate or "ethereal" substances which his contemporaries saw everywhere and explained physical phenomena by the movements of the particles of substances or particles of the ether. Lomonosov conceived of the ether as being also composed of separate but extremely small particles. In his opinion it was the most delicate form of matter, capable to the highest degree of every type of motion producing heat and light; its particles must be in contact with each other, since only in this way could the terrific speed of the radiation of light be explained.

The question of the nature of light, like the question of the essence of electricity and other physical phenomena, had already occupied scholars for a long time. But a tolerably satisfactory solution to the question was, of course, possible only after a knowledge of the properties of light, which were studied with such thoroughness by Sir Isaac Newton in the third quarter of the seventeenth century. It was he who advanced the first theory supported by facts. Newton assumed that the luminous body emits small particles of light-substance, which perform all the functions peculiar to a ray of light. Even at that time such an explanation of the phenomena of light was acknowledged to be unsatisfactory in many respects. Thus the reflection of light was explained by the repulsion of the particles of the light-substances, while its refraction, on the other hand, was held to be due to attraction between the particles of the light-substance and the particles of the refracting body. Newton himself was not satisfied with his theory and published it only on the insistence of his friends.

Therefore another theory of the radiation of light appeared at the end of the seventeenth century—the wave theory, first expounded clearly and thoroughly by Christian Huygens. He believed the entire universe to be full of a very fine mobile substance which penetrates all matter—the ether; its wavelike motion is what we call light. If a disturbance in equilibrium takes place somewhere in the ether, a wave arises like the wavy motion in water when a stone is thrown into it. Then special waves of ether go out from this spot, conditioned by the vibration of its particles, which are analogous to the vibration of the particles of air during the diffusion of waves of sound.

Of these two theories Lomonosov recognized only that of Huygens, in spite of the fact that almost all the physicists of the eighteenth century considered Newton's authority infallible and held strongly to the "matter of light" and the theory of effluxion. Lomonosov expounded his views on the nature of light in detail in a public speech which he delivered at the solemn assembly of the Academy of Sciences on July 1, 1756, the *Oration on the Origin of Light, Presenting a New Theory of Colors*, and in the earlier *Oration on Aerial Phenomena Produced by the Force of Electricity*, given on November 26, 1753, of which I shall speak in more detail in the next chapter. Here he describes at length those vibrating movements of the particles of the ether which constitute light waves. Thus, regarding the question of the nature of light, Lomonosov is in accord with the physicists of the nineteenth century. The theory of effluxion, like the "matter of fire," was notable for its vitality and was abandoned only after the work of Jong (1800) and (especially) Frenelle (1820), in favor of the wave theory in the first half of the last century.

Lomonosov's works in physics are much less numerous in the last years of his life, for at that time he interested himself, as we shall see, in other branches of learning. I shall mention only his treatise on the solid and liquid states of substances (delivered on September 6, 1760, before a public session of the Academy of Sciences), which now, except for a few passages, does not present much interest. One of these passages will be examined later; another, which we shall dwell on here, has to do with an observation which in its time was of extreme interest to all the scholars of the period. In December 1759 Academician A. Braun was successful for the first time in freezing mercury and made a report of this feat before the public session of the academy just mentioned. He made his experiments in collaboration with Lomonosov, who also described certain ones of them.

In December 1759 there were very severe frosts in St. Petersburg, such as had not occurred for several decades. On December 14 the cold reached 205° on the Delisle thermometer (of which I shall speak further; this would be −37°C), and on this day Braun investigated "how much it is possible to increase this natural cold by artificial means." His experiments showed that in such cold the ice of "strong water" (nitric acid) registered 234°D, which was extremely good since Fahrenheit was unable to get a greater cold than —40°F or 210°D. During this experiment Braun noticed that little bubbles of air were visible in the mercury of the thermometer used to measure the temperature. These could only result from the fact that the mercury itself had frozen. He decided to break the thermometer in the succeeding experiments and thus to verify the hypothesis.

The next experiment was made on December 25, 1759, with cold on the street at 199°D. The mercury thermometer, which had been plunged into a freezing mixture, was broken, and Braun was the first to obtain a sphere of solid mercury. It seemed soft, like lead, and looked like polished silver. On December 26 the experiments were continued, with Lomonosov participating. The cold became steadily more intense and at ten in the morning the temperature reached 212°D (—41¼°C). Then the mercury thermometer was plunged into a freezing mixture of snow, "strong water" (nitric acid), and vitriolic oil (sulphuric acid). Lomonosov describes the further progress of the experiment thus: "Having no doubt that it had already frozen, I quickly struck the bulb with a brass compass that was there. Immediately thereupon the glass shell shattered and fell away from the pellet of mercury which remained, and attached to which was a little tail like a pure silver wire, as pliable as soft metal and about one-fourth of a line in thickness, formed by the mercury that had been in the tube of the thermometer. When I then struck the mercury pellet with a hammer it felt about as hard as lead or tin. With each blow, from the first to the fourth, the pellet was compressed without cracks, but with the fifth, sixth, and seventh blows small cracks appeared. . . . I then ceased to hammer the mercury and began to cut it with a knife. Within about twenty minutes it became a soft amalgam or paste, and soon thereafter recovered its original liquid form—that is, it melted in the extreme cold of 208°D."

The temperatures reached in the experiments of Braun and Lomonosov were the lowest to be obtained until such time as experimenters began to compress gases. (The first to be compressed was sulphur dioxide, obtained in a liquid form by Monge and Clouet in 1780; the second was chlorine. Northmore was the first to obtain liquid chlorine, in 1806, and then later Faraday in 1823.) The lowest temperatures are obtained by the evaporation of gases not under atmospheric pressure but under greatly diminished pressure. In our day compressed helium serves this purpose, and by its help Kamerlingh Onnes in his laboratory in the Netherlands has obtained a temperature only a few tenths of a degree above absolute zero.

Before closing this chapter more should be said about the thermometers used in the middle of the eighteenth century, particularly those used by Lomonosov. At that time the thermometer of Delisle was most widely used in Russia (it was employed in the experiments of Braun and Lomonosov just described); Fahrenheit's was less used. Lomonosov also used his own thermometer, which he distinguishes by the word "ours." Instruments for measuring temperatures by observing the expansion of air, which received the name of thermometers, evidently owe their origin to Galileo, who in 1592 was the first to construct such a thermometer. The first thermometers were very imperfect—their readings never coincide—and it was only toward the end of the seventeenth century that they began to be reliable.

Relatively trustworthy thermometers, earlier than others, were prepared by Daniel Fahrenheit at the very beginning of the eighteenth century. His first thermometers made use of alcohol, which proved to be defective in that its coefficient of expansion changes with the temperature. From 1720 on, Fahrenheit began to make mercury thermometers.

He made use of the following points for his scale: (a) the temperature induced by a mixture of ice, water, sal ammoniac, and cooking salt, the lowest temperature then known, which was designated as 0°; (b) the melting point of ice, designated as 32°; (c) the temperature of the human body (96°). The boiling point of water under normal pressure then corresponded to 212° on Fahrenheit's scale, and consequently the scale of his thermometer was defined by two points, the melting point of ice and the boiling point of water. This thermometer soon became widely used in Western Europe, but was later displaced by the thermometer of Réaumur, which bears his name. At the present time the Fahrenheit thermometer remains in use only in England and its colonies and in the United States.

René Antoine Réaumur, the well-known naturalist, worked on thermometers from 1730 to 1733. He proposed to make use of the relative expansion of liquids in a thermometer to measure temperatures. Taking the volume of a liquid, wine spirits, as 1,000 at the constant temperature of the melting of ice, he marked on a scale above and below zero thousandth parts of this volume. Each such division constituted one degree. Immersing his thermometer in boiling water, he found that the alcohol rose to the 1,080th point and took this as the boiling point of water, forgetting that alcohol boils at a temperature 20° lower than water. Deluc in 1743, following Celsius' work, was the first to construct a mercury thermometer with the scale which was named after Réaumur. However, his scale has nothing in common with the one proposed by Réaumur since it is divided between two points—the melting of ice (0°) and the boiling of water (80°).

N. O. Delisle, a member of the St. Petersburg Academy of Sciences, began to work on thermometers in 1731 and described his scale in detail in the academy reports in 1733. He made use of mercury and, like Réaumur, one constant point—the boiling point of water. He divided the volume of mercury at this point into 100,000 parts in a "large thermometer" and 10,000 parts in a "small thermometer," and placed the corresponding divisions on the scale. The mercury of the small thermometer went down to the 150th division in melting ice, that is, its volume decreased by 150/10,000. Delisle equipped his brother with thermometers of this kind when he went on an expedition to Siberia, with the result that Siberian cold was recorded for the first time. (The thermometers were open, so that they had to be held in a vertical position.)

In 1742 Celsius advanced the idea of welding up the glass tube of the mercury thermometer and of marking the degrees of its scale in accordance with two constant points, the melting of ice and the boiling of water, dividing the space between them into a hundred equal parts. This scale, too, has nothing in common with that now called after Celsius. The latter (boiling point of water, 100°, freezing point, 0°) was first advanced by the French physicist Cristaine in 1743 and later by the very famous natural philosopher Linnaeus in 1745. It should be called the centigrade scale, the abbreviation for which is the letter C. After Celsius' work all thermometers began to be made according to his instructions. In France they were made by Deluc, as has already been said. In Russia, on the thermometer of Delisle, the temperature of the melting point of ice is taken at 150°, the boiling point of water at 0°, so that states of cold (freezing) were measured by a larger number of degrees.

Lomonosov's thermometer combined all the improvements introduced by his predecessors. He ordered the first ten thermometers of this kind in May 1752, and began to use them at the beginning of 1753. A description of them does not exist, but I have been able to reconstruct Lomonosov's scale from several passages in his works, of which the most important is the *Oration on Aerial Phenomena*

produced by the Force of Electricity (1753) where, in one
of the supplements, he writes as follows: "Sea water covered
with ice, 28 sazhen[1] in depth, 23 versts from shore in the
Finnish Gulf, registered 150°, or the freezing point—according to my system of division, 0°—on a thermometer which
had been immersed in it for half an hour. . . . I put sea
water which I had received from North Cape in a glass set
out in the cold air on February 14. When the mercury went
down to 2° below the point of freezing, a dense formation
of needles appeared in the water. And when it reached 3½°
below, all of the water solidified. In the air, the thermometer
registered 177°, or 27° lower than the freezing point." It is
evident from this that Lomonosov's 0° is equal to 0° on
the centigrade thermometer, the boiling point of water is
150°, and each degree on Lomonosov's scale is equal to a
degree on Delisle's, or two-thirds of a degree on the centigrade thermometer.

[1] 1 sazhen equals 7 feet. ED.

CHAPTER 4

Chief events of Lomonosov's life from 1749-1757—Eulogistic orations—Tragedies—Lomonosov's communications to I. I. Shuvalov—His work in history—Conflicts —The new statutes of the academy—The University of Moscow—A Hymn to the Beard—His own house—Atmospheric electricity—Thunder machine and the death of G. Richmann—The speech about atmospheric phenomena proceeding from electrical force—The theory of the production of electricity—Northern lights—Colored glass—The letter about the benefits of glass—Trip to Moscow—The glass factory—Mosaic pictures—The Battle of Poltava.

THE period of Lomonosov's activity from 1749 to 1756 might be called a chemical epoch in view of the chief subject with which he was occupied at that time. But since his amazing versatility is just as clearly apparent in this period as earlier, I shall first dwell upon several outstanding features of his work in other departments of pure and applied science so that I may review all that he did in the line of chemistry in the next chapter.

In 1749, the Academy of Sciences began to prepare for a great event in its life; a "public assembly," that is, a solemn public session, was to take place for the first time after a long interruption of the custom. It was not easy to find orators for this assembly; as Schumacher wrote to G. N. Teplov, who was with the president in Moscow, the historian Miller could be one of the speakers; as for the second, although he very much wished to do without Lomonosov, there was no one to put in his place. One academician was not suitable on account of his physique; the voice of a second was too weak; a third did not know Russian; a fourth was engaged in an unpleasant lawsuit; and a fifth had a mistress of low origin. The president of the academy, who was then with the court in Moscow, agreed with Schumacher's arguments and appointed Miller and Lomonosov as the orators.

For the first time, on November 25, 1749, Lomonosov appeared in a public assembly of the Academy of Sciences with a speech in the Russian language, an oration in eulogy of the Empress Elizabeth Petrovna on the day of her accession to the throne. He was of imposing appearance, possessed a loud voice, and spoke well and expressively; his oration created an excellent impression and was well received at court. Later on, at other assemblies, he delivered similar orations. Of these the best, by reason of the unquestioned sincerity of its sentiments, was the speech in praise of Peter the Great delivered by Lomonosov on April 26, 1755. Evidently these orations pleased the general public as much as the court, and at one time they were considered almost an indispensable appurtenance of the public assemblies of the academy.

It should be said that Lomonosov considered Peter I one of the very greatest of sovereigns, the ideal toward which all rulers should strive. Probably this feeling was due to the influence of Christian Wolf, who knew Peter personally and had performed numerous commissions for him. Then, too, in his childhood Lomonosov had undoubtedly heard a good many stories about Peter's visits to the north, his visits with Bazhenin on the Vavchuzhny wharf, and the like. Every time he speaks of Peter he presents him as a hero, brings forward the positive sides of his reign, and does not touch on the darker aspects. In the later years of his life he began to write a great heroic poem about Peter, the first two songs of which describe his journey to the north, his battles with the Swedes, and the dangers to which the monarch was subjected.

Soon after his return from abroad, Lomonosov had already won renown as a poet who fulfilled excellently the obligation of presenting festival odes—odes on the occasion of the birthdays, name-days, and the accession to the throne of ruling personages. His reputation became established as a poet who was always ready to present specimens of his art. For this reason he was sometimes given extra commissions by the court, for which he had to lay aside all other business.

When in the year 1750 the Russian theater and plays written exclusively by Russian authors came into fashion, it was decided by the authorities to make up for the paucity of the repertoire of the time with tragedies by Lomonosov. And here we find a note of September 29, 1750, in the journal of the chancellery of the Academy of Sciences: "On this date the Lord President of the Academy of Sciences announced an oral ukase from Her Imperial Majesty by which it was ordered him, the Lord President: that professors Tredyakovsky and Lomonosov should compose tragedies and report thereon to them in the chancellery." Lomonosov applied himself forthwith to the commission: in the notebook of his first tragedy, *Tamira and Selim*, stands the inscription: "Begun on September 29 after dinner." He finished it in four weeks, and on November 1 the academy directed that six hundred copies should be printed at once. Since a new edition was required as early as January 1751, the tragedy evidently pleased the contemporary public.

In 1751 Lomonosov wrote a second tragedy, *Demofont*. These two plays, along with those of Sumarokov and Tredyakovsky, are the first Russian dramas to be written in imitation of French works, and can be considered today only from this point of view. The influence of the school dramas which he studied at some time in the Slavo-Graeco-

Latin Academy is evident in places in Lomonosov's tragedies, but the chief influence is found in the tragedies of the
French classical school, to which he strongly adhered in
both plays.

Lomonosov's elevation to the rank of a collegiate councillor, with an increase of stipend to 1,200 rubles a year, was
brought to pass in March 1751, probably not without the
mediation of Ivan Ivanovich Shuvalov. This grandee became the favorite of Elizabeth probably at the end of 1749,
when he was appointed *kammerjunker*.[1] At this time Shuvalov also became a patron of Lomonosov, from whom he
took lessons in Russian versification. On August 18, 1750,
Lomonosov wrote him a rhymed letter, from which I quote
a few lines to show the closeness of their relation:

> I only move 'mid walls, and by the fire;
> Find comfort when of summertime I write—
> Of summer—yet it faileth to inspire,
> In a lone revery I seek delight.
> But spring returns with summer, nonetheless,
> In winter I enjoy their beauty when
> My soul is heartened by thy friendliness
> That I would show Parnassus by my pen.

Shortly after this letter, Lomonosov received from Elizabeth, dated August 27, from Tsarskoye Selo (now Pushkin)
some remuneration or other for which he thanked her in an
ode. In it the Empress' hunt is described, and lines remarkable for their expressiveness occur:

> Trenches, or knot of branches dense
> The horse's course do not impair:
> He clangs his bit, and twists his head,
> And stamps with wild and stormy tread
> And glories in his rider fair.

[1] Groom of the bed chamber, rank just below court chamberlain
(*kammerherr*). ED.

Lomonosov had several "eminent patrons" of this kind. They never let pass an opportunity to put before him the idea that, from their point of view, it would be much more suitable for him to abandon the exact sciences and to occupy himself only with Russian literature and history. Apropos of this, Lomonosov wrote a letter to Shuvalov on January 4, 1753, containing curious details about the life of the academicians of this period.

Here are some excerpts from this letter: "And as for my other occupations in physics and chemistry, there is neither need nor possibility that I forsake them. Every man needs relaxation from his labors; for that purpose he leaves serious business and seeks to pass the time with guests or members of his household at cards, checkers, and other entertainments, and some with tobacco smoke, which I have given up long since, finding nothing but boredom in it. And thus I trust that I shall be allowed several hours a day to relax from the labors which I have expended on the collection and composition of Russian history and on the beautification of the Russian tongue so that I may use these hours, rather than for billiards, for experiments in physics and chemistry. These serve me not only as a change of matter in place of amusement but furnish movement instead of medicine, and, moreover, can certainly bring profit and honor to my fatherland hardly less than my first occupation. Before closing my very humble petition, as regards the factory, do not think that it will hinder me, respected sir, since with this have come to an end all of my great chemical labors, which I have carried on for three years and which it would be unbearable torture for me to lose fruitlessly, and a much greater impediment than that to be feared from the labors themselves." The factory mentioned in this letter will be discussed later in the chapter.

Characteristic of this period are the very numerous conflicts which Lomonosov had with certain academicians and other personages. Practically no mention is made of them during the four or five years which followed the termination of Lomonosov's arrest in January 1744. In 1748 he began to take part in the historical assembly of the academy, and there he disagreed particularly with the historiographer Miller on the subject of the communication of historical data. Each considered his views immutable; consequently their quarrels often passed from the scientific into the personal. Lomonosov had conflicts also with his laboratory assistant, Bittiger, who lived in the same house, which belonged to the academy, and was evidently distinguished by his expansive and licentious mode of life. On May 10, 1756, Lomonosov wrote of him thus:

"The disturbance on the part of the great number of guests of various professions and nations who came to his quarters almost day and night grew so great that drunken guests broke down the gates even in the middle of the day, and often at night these gates served as pavement for the calashes and cabriolets that came. More than that, unjust and insolent wrongs were committed against my family by his servant girls, for not long since his wench sent my daughter away from the staircase with infamous words. And when my wife came out and asked why that wench was acting thus, then she, turning her back and leaning on the railing, gave rude answers. . . ." This affair ended simply when Bittiger was dismissed by the chancellery on Lomonosov's complaints.

Even more serious were Lomonosov's constant conflicts with enemies among the academicians in general and with the chancellery of the academy, where, as in the past, the all-powerful Schumacher (who by this time had even taken in his son-in-law, Taubert, to assist him) was ensconced. On the frequent absences of the president of the academy, who at that time was also hetman of the Zaporogian cossacks, these two, as before, actually decided everything. In all these encounters one curious peculiarity was noticeable: Lomonosov in the main took up the cudgels against those who were "persecutors of the sciences" and who hindered the propagation of education in Russia, and not against foreigners in general or against the Germans, many of whom were his friends. Seeing that he could do nothing alone under the regulations existing in the academy, on December 30, 1754, he asked Shuvalov "to promote him in the academy in order to put a stop to crafty undertakings," and, if that were not possible, to transfer him into another body, preferably into the Foreign Office, "so that all should say: 'the stone which the builders refused is become the head of the corner. This is the Lord's doing.' Or so that in my departure from the academy it should be made perfectly clear of what it was being deprived in losing such a man, who has embellished it for so many years and has always struggled with the persecutors of learning, regardless of the danger to himself."

Thus it is evident that Lomonosov had no low opinion of himself—and his high opinion was perfectly natural. An excellent scientific education which he received from Christian Wolf at Marburg, genius, exceptional versatility, and rich scientific vision (which manifested itself, for example, in his works in physics) made Lomonosov a scholar of the first rank, excelling other scholars of his time both in his knowledge and in the vitality of his scientific ideas.

To the commission formed in the academy to develop material for the new statute of the academy in 1755, Lomonosov presented a lengthy "opinion" on the superfluities and lacks of the academy and how to correct them. In it, among other things, he speaks out against prohibiting from study those persons who were subject to the poll tax. "As if forty altyn were a sum so great and weighty to the treasury that it would be a pity to lose it in order to obtain one native Russian scholar—and better to order a foreigner from abroad! It would be enough to make this one exception: not to include the children of serfs." This opinion of his, however, was not taken under consideration, for in one of the very first sessions of the commission he quarreled so violently with Adjunct V. Teplov (who had been tutor to the children of Count Razumovsky) about establishing an office of vice-president, which Lomonosov had evidently marked out for himself, that there were no more sessions. The president of the academy, when he was informed of what had taken place, wanted to deliver a severe reprimand to Lomonosov. This offended Lomonosov deeply, and at once he wrote a letter to Shuvalov asking his protection from such "abuse and unjust defamation." The letter had its results, and the written reprimand was destroyed.

Lomonosov himself, under the influence of what had taken place, wrote a long report on the status of the academy in which, among other matters, he inserted expressions characteristic of the director, such as: "I made a great mistake in policy when I made Lomonosov a professor"; and of his son-in-law Taubert, "Do we need ten Lomonosovs? Even one is a burden to us." He proposed a series of practical measures to improve the academy, such as not to permit persons with little education to control the sciences, not to give power to foreigners who bore a grudge against native Russian scholars, and the like.

Gradually not only Lomonosov, but many other academicians as well, submitted complaints to the chancellery. It was probably to calm their spirits that the president, when about to make a journey to Little Russia in 1757, gave instructions that, because of Schumacher's frail health, "Lomonosov should serve with him in joint authority and countersign all business matters." It was actually on March 1 that Lomonosov entered upon his new duties. He took on various additional responsibilities thereby, and functioned pretty autocratically.

Another of Lomonosov's noteworthy achievements was his contribution to the founding of the University of Moscow. In his incessant labors for the propagation of education in Russia, he often pointed out to Shuvalov that it was necessary to found a university in Moscow, and on principles as liberal as possible. Shuvalov, in the fulfillment of this noble project, constantly asked advice of Lomonosov, who drew up detailed notes for him. According to Lomonosov's view, the plan of the university should be broad enough so that in the future, when the university had developed, there should be an adequate staff of professors, although at first it would only be possible to invite a part of them. Thus there would be left sums of money free to use on auxiliary institutes, and above all on a library. Therefore it was proposed that the number of professors should not be less than twelve: three on the medical faculty, three on the faculty of jurisprudence, and six on the philosophical faculty.

In all probability, the elaborately conceived project which was presented by Shuvalov to the senate also belonged to Lomonosov. All necessary legal steps were taken without delay, and the university was formally opened by Shuvalov on January 12, 1755, St. Tatiana's day. Unquestionably Lomonosov was the real founder of the oldest Russian university, although evidently he took no part in the opening itself. The first professors of the new university were several of his students. One of the first books published by the printing house founded in connection with the University of Moscow was the second edition of a collection of Lomonosov's works, printed by the order of Shuvalov. (The first volume appeared in 1757; the second in 1759.) This showed how highly he esteemed Lomonosov.

Shuvalov asked Lomonosov to compose a rhymed signature for the portrait of the author which appeared in the collection—a portrait of special value because it gives us a dated picture of him. But he answered, "I by no means wish that, honored sir: I am mortified that an engraving of myself is to appear. I ask only that which is just and proper for me, that which Her Most Gracious Majesty deigns usually to bestow on her devoted slaves—what is fitting according to my service and my career, and what is more necessary and profitable for my fatherland than for me." Nevertheless, there is an inscription below the portrait which is attributed to Shuvalov; if this is true, evidently Lomonosov's labors in teaching him versification were not in vain. (The first edition of Lomonosov's verses was published by the Academy of Sciences in 1751.)

Early in 1757 some verses of unknown composition entitled A *Hymn to the Beard* began to circulate among St. Petersburg dwellers. The clergy, privileged to wear beards in eighteenth-century Russia, were lampooned in ten verses as "sacrificial priests" who covered themselves with beards as "a curtain for their false ideas." Soon it became known that Lomonosov was the author of this piece, and a little later he wrote a second poem in which evidently he expressed his amusement at the alarm produced among the clergy by his hymn. ("Oh dear! oh horror! oh thunder! you are pulling at the trousers which hang beneath Satan's mouth. See, he is raging and growing angry. . . .") And while in the hymn the clergy are mentioned only anonymously, verses in the second poem, such as "Little kids are born with beards—how they are respected among priests!" leave no doubt as to the references intended by the hymn.

Such was the impression produced on the clergy by the hymn that as early as March 1757 the synod made a report to Elizabeth signed by four "humble pilgrims." In it Lomonosov was accused of "blasphemy of the mystery of the Holy Baptism" (each verse of the hymn included a refrain with this reference to the beard, "It is a pity that thou art not baptized, and that thou, therefore, preferest the shameful part of the body which is preferable to Hell") and "of the teachings of the Holy Fathers. This lampooner, in the guise of an Old Believer[2] has written most obscene abuse against Christian conscience and honor about all persons generally, both those who formerly had beards and those who have them now . . . and, not satisfied with that, shortly afterward he published another such libel on the nation in which, among many flagrant abuses of the clerical office, he set up unreasoning kids as to be far more respected than priests." At the end of the report the synod asked "that such seductive and abusive lampoons be destroyed and burnt publicly by your most exalted decree, and that it be forbidden to perpetrate them in the future, and that the designated Lomonosov be dispatched to the synod for the exhortation and correction that is his due."

This report had no harmful consequences for Lomonosov since Elizabeth took no action upon it. But letters of a polemic character soon appeared in public, evidently proceeding from the ranks of the clergy, repeating the same strains as those in the report of the synod. They appeared under the signature of Christofor Zubnitsky: it is not known who was concealed under this pseudonym. Furthermore, a number of poems of Lomonosov's literary opponents, Sumarokov and Tredyakovsky, were published stressing Lomonosov's fondness for drink—as, for example, the *Hymn to a Drunken Head.*

It is pertinent at this juncture to discuss Lomonosov's relation to the questions of religion and the Church. From his poems and other works it is clear that he was a deist who accepted the prevalent rationalist doctrine: that is, he acknowledged one of the bourgeois forms of Christianity. Lomonosov's God was synonymous with nature, the creator of the world, and the like. The interrelation of science and religion he expressed thus: "The sacred writings cannot everywhere be interpreted in a literal sense, but in a rhetori-

[2] Dissenter. ED.

cal one; one cannot learn astronomy and other sciences from them." He had a rather negative attitude toward the clergy and priests both before the *Hymn to the Beard* and thereafter; this was undoubtedly well known to the ecclesiastical authorities. St. Petersburg preachers of the time often spoke against "naturalists" in their sermons, and unquestionably had Lomonosov in mind. It was not without reason that in 1760 he wished to insert the following among the privileges of the university: "That the clergy should not cavil at teachings which demonstrate the truths of nature for improvement and enlightenment, and in particular should not vilify the sciences in their sermons."

This attitude of Lomonosov toward the clergy, and his rallying to the defense of the freedom of research against the "cloaks for false opinions" was probably in part an expression of the view of his exalted patrons; but it undoubtedly harmonized with his own views, which he expressed bravely as the foremost intellectual of his time.

As P. N. Berkov points out, the literary polemic occasioned by the *Hymn to the Beard* must be regarded as one of the stages of the struggle between two systems of ideology striving for ascendancy within the ruling class. One was religious, a relic of the feudal past attempting to adapt itself to new conditions; the other was scientific, a product of the new bourgeois conditions in the West, which proposed a compromise solution of the religious question by affirming the validity of religious faith without reference to the clergy.

In 1756 Lomonosov came into free possession of six burned out places on the right bank of the Moika Canal, not far from the present Pochtamsky bridge, with the stipulation that within five years he build a stone house on the site. Lomonosov set about building at once, and erected a stone house of moderate size, with a laboratory and a flight of wide steps, where he always dined in summer and entertained his fellow countrymen from the seacoast, who never failed to visit him when they arrived in St. Petersburg with their wares. He moved into his own house in 1757.

During this period of Lomonosov's scientific activity his electrical experiments were of outstanding significance. In North America, about the middle of the eighteenth century, Benjamin Franklin was actively studying the nature and properties of electricity. His experiments led him to realize the truth of the idea expressed by many before him that thunderclouds are electrically charged and that there is in them the same kind of electricity as that generated by machines or produced in the Leyden jar, which was discovered about 1745. Franklin proposed to decide the question as to whether clouds were electrified in this manner: A man standing isolated on a high spot would hold a piece of iron which had been drawn to a sharp point. If, when pointed directly at the overhanging cloud, the iron became electrified, that would be proof of the presence of electricity in the cloud. Franklin himself did not perform this experiment, but the French physicist Dalibard set up near Paris an iron pole forty feet high, partly insulated by a wooden support. When on May 10, 1752, a thundercloud came over this pole, it was electrified so strongly that it discharged sparks four centimeters in length. In June of the same year (1752) Franklin, knowing nothing of Dalibarre's experiments, released a silk kite below a cloud. A metal point was made fast to the kite, and to the point was tied a hemp rope by which the kite was held. On the lower end of the rope was attached a key, and to the key a silk string, which insulated the whole system. When the rope became wet with rain, sparks could be drawn from the key. In this manner it was proved that clouds are electrified and that lightning is an electric spark.

People in St. Petersburg learned very soon of Franklin's experiments, and one of the academicians, G. V. Richmann, who had long worked on electricity, repeated them and inserted a description of them in the *St. Petersburg News*. He put an iron rod six feet long through a bottle with a broken bottom, attached an iron wire to the end of the rod, and brought it insulated into a room; to the end of the wire he hung freely an iron ruler, and to the upper end of the ruler a silken thread. When the electricity was in the wire, the thread moved away from the metal ruler, "running after the finger." On July 18, during a thunderstorm, sparks could be drawn from the ruler, and many of Richmann's guests made this experiment. The whole apparatus received the name of a "thunder machine" and was set up in many homes; Lomonosov among others made one for himself in his official dwelling.

In the next year, 1753, Richmann continued his experiments and submitted accounts of them to the *St. Petersburg News*. Lomonosov, as Richmann's closest friend, also took part in them, and both prepared to speak on electricity in the formal session of the academy. During a session of the academy conference on July 26 of that year, Richmann observed that a thundercloud was coming close, and hastened to his home, which was on the corner of the fifth line and Grand Avenue on Vasilyevsky Island. He wanted to show the electrical phenomena to the master of engraving at the academy, Sokolov, in order to have a drawing made. Sokolov tells what happened later thus: "When the professor had looked at the electric indicator he judged that the thunder was still far off and believed that there was no immediate danger; however, when it came very close, there might be danger. Shortly after that the professor, who was standing a foot away from the iron rod, looked at the electric indicator again; just then a palish blue ball of fire, as big as a fist, came out of the rod without any contact whatsoever. It went right to the forehead of the professor, who in that instant fell back without uttering a sound onto a box standing behind him. At the very same moment followed a bang like the discharge of a small cannon, whereat the master of engraving fell to the ground and felt several blows on his back. It was later discovered that they came from the wire, which was torn to pieces and which left burned stripes on his caftan from shoulder to skirt."

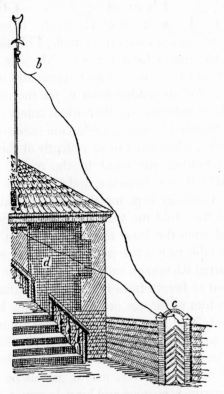

Lightning rod on Lomonosov's house.

Lomonosov described this event in a letter to Shuvalov in such beautiful clear language that it ought to be quoted.

"Gracious sir, Ivan Ivanovich, you will consider what I am now writing to your excellency a marvel, since the dead do not write. I still do not know—at least I doubt whether I am alive or dead. I see that Professor Richmann was killed by thunder under circumstances precisely like those under which I was working at the very same time. On the 26th of this July at one o'clock in the afternoon, a thundercloud came up from the north. The thunder was remarkable for its force, without a drop of rain. Looking at the thunder machine which had been set up, I saw not the slightest indication of the presence of electricity. However, while they were putting the food on the table, I obtained extraordinary electric sparks from the wire. My wife and others approached and they as well as I repeatedly touched the wire and the rod suspended from it, for the reason that I wished to have witnesses see the various colors of fire about which the departed Professor Richmann used to argue with me. Suddenly it thundered most violently at the exact time that I was holding my hand to the metal, and sparks crackled. All fled away from me, and my wife implored that I go away. Curiosity kept me there two or three minutes more, until they told me that the soup was getting cold. But by that time the force of electricity greatly subsided. I had sat at table only a few minutes when the man servant of the departed Richmann suddenly opened the door, all in tears and out of breath from fear. I thought that some one had beaten him as he was on his way to me, but he said, with difficulty, that the professor had been injured by thunder. Going to his home with the greatest possible speed my strength allowed, I arrived to see him lying lifeless. His poor widow and her mother were just as pale as he. The death which I so narrowly escaped and his pale corpse, the thought of our friendship, the weeping of his wife, his children, and his household, affected me so deeply that I could say nothing and give no answer to the great number of people who had assembled as I looked at that person with whom I had sat in conference an hour ago and discussed our future public convocation. The first blow from the suspended ruler with the thread fell on his head, where a cherry-red spot was visible on his forehead; but the electric force of the thunder had passed out of his feet into the floor boards. His feet and fingers were blue and his shoe torn but not burned through. We tried to restore the movement of the blood in him, since he was still warm; however, his head was injured and there was no further hope. And thus he verified, by a lamentable experiment, the fact that it is possible to draw off the electric force of thunder; this must be by directing it, however, onto an iron staff which should stand in an empty place where the thunder can strike as much as it wishes. Nonetheless, Mr. Richmann died a splendid death, fulfilling a duty of his profession. His memory will never die; but his poor widow, his mother-in-law, and his five-year-old son, who has shown much promise, and his two daughters, one about two years old and the other about six months, weep both for him and for their own great misfortune. Therefore, your excellency, I implore you as a true lover and patron of science to be their gracious helper in order that the poor widow of the estimable professor shall have sustenance until her death, and that she may educate the little son of Richmann to be such a lover of the sciences as was his father. Richmann's salary was 860 rubles; most gracious sir, obtain this pension for the poor widow or for her children until death! The Lord God will reward you for this good deed, and I would esteem it more than if it were for myself. Furthermore, in order that this incident should not be publicly interpreted to the detriment of the growth of the sciences, I most humbly beg you to have pity upon science and upon your excellency's very humble servant, Mikhail Lomonosov, who is now in tears."

Regardless of what had transpired the public convocation of the academy was set for November 25, 1753. Lomonosov prepared a long speech for it, which like all speeches was examined by the conference beforehand. Lomonosov had to reply to the doubts in the minds of members who had read the speech and considered that some of his ideas had been expressed earlier by other people. This speech bore the title, *Oration on Aerial Phenomena, proceeding from the Force of Electricity, presented by Mikhail Lomonosov.* The chief point of this oration lies in the theory he advances on the formation of electricity in the air.

While horizontal movements of the air, i.e. winds, do not produce "electricity," vertical movements, i.e. ascending and descending air currents, may, because of the friction of the particles of vapor, give rise to "electricity." These rising

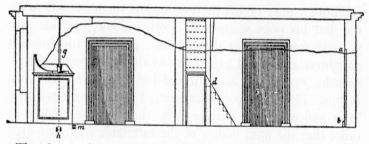

Thunder machine at Richmann's house. *h*—spot where Richmann stood at the moment the lightning struck; *m*—spot where Sokolov stood.

and descending currents of air, which were apparently unnoticed until Lomonosov's time, unquestionably exist and were described later by Humboldt in the beginning of the nineteenth century. It is by the falling of the cold upper air, which is much heavier than the warmer lower air, that the great frosts which sometimes begin suddenly after a thaw in the winter can be explained. Thunderstorms occur most often from three to four o'clock in the afternoon, because at that time the lower part of the atmosphere is more heated and rises more easily and swiftly. The "electric" phenomena of a thunderstorm are lightning, accompanied by thunder, and sheet lightning. Much rarer is the appearance of "electricity" without thunderclouds (this was noted by Lomonosov on his thunder machine on April 26, 1753). The thunder machine shows that sometimes when the thundercloud rises the "electric force" reaches the earth; but when "electricity" does not reach the earth, then the cloud transfers its force to the earth sharply by lightning and thunder. To avert lightning it is worth while to set up "electric arrows" in places removed from the dwelling to conduct the lightning into the earth. In conclusion, the aurora borealis, which usually occurs when great cold is setting in, that is, when the upper cold atmosphere sinks into the lower, is probably also the result of "electric force."

In order to confirm his ideas about the rising and descending currents of air, Lomonosov made numerous researches in 1751 and 1752 on the density of air under various temperatures. These experiments fully confirmed the correctness of his opinions. The theory of the sinking of the upper atmosphere, as a result of which a cold wave is observed, was proposed by Prof. Elias Loomis in the United States in the 1870's. Its experimental proof was made in 1879-1881 by the chemist E. Morley: since oxygen is heavier than nitrogen, therefore in the upper atmosphere the quantity of the first in proportion to the quantity of the second is less than on the surface of the earth. Exact analyses show that the "cold wave," the present polar front, is accompanied by a very slight decrease in the quantity of oxygen in the air. The sinking of the cold upper air was finally demonstrated only by means of balloon probes at the beginning of the twentieth century.

All his life Lomonosov took an interest in thunderstorms: he took notes on them constantly and noted the characteristics of lightning. In 1756 he began to write his great work, *The Theory of Electricity, Evolved by Means of Mathematics*. In the first two chapters, following a discussion of the properties of the ether we find the basis of his theory, which consists of the proposition that electricity is a very fast rotary movement of the particles of the ether.

In like manner all his life Lomonosov made observations of the northern lights, but the work he undertook, which was very large in its conception, *An Examination of the Causes of the Northern Lights,* was hardly even begun. Only two paragraphs were written down. Lomonosov made a drawing of every display of northern lights of any importance; from these drawings he gradually made engravings which were to have been included in the *Examination of the Causes.* These were found in the archives—eleven copper plates in all with four drawings engraved on each, save one which bore only three. These engravings are very finely done and show Lomonosov's great skill in draftsmanship. All the drawings are included in the sixth volume of the collection of Lomonosov's works which appeared in 1934.

Only one display of northern lights was described in detail by Lomonosov in the *Oration on Aerial Phenomena, proceeding from the Force of Electricity.* This was the display which took place on January 23, 1750. It is depicted on one of the copper plates and in the table attached to the *Oration.*

In close connection with the observations just described, quite naturally stands Lomonosov's constant preoccupation with meteorology. His lively interest in this subject undoubtedly dates from the days of his youth, when the success of his business depended on the weather. In him we have a meteorologist of the end of the nineteenth century. He sought continually to set up self-recording instruments and has left us descriptions of many of them; on his property (about which I shall speak) he intended to construct a self-recording meteorological observatory, of which, however, no description has been preserved. In his later work, the *Speech on Greater Accuracy in Navigation* (1759), there is reference to a large number of new forms of apparatus. Lomonosov also understood the importance of investigating the upper strata of the atmosphere (which was achieved only at the end of the nineteenth century) and built a machine to carry a self-recording thermometer into the upper strata of the atmosphere. But the machine would not fly when submitted to a test.

Thus far Lomonosov's occupations which did not require a chemical laboratory have been discussed. The remainder of this chapter will be given to a description of the important purely practical work which he accomplished in the laboratory and its consequences. From 1749 on, this work was extremely intensive; in the register of the sessions of the conference of this period we constantly find Lomonosov's absence thus noted: "Very busy in the laboratory."

The matter which interested him so much at this time, and evidently his noble patrons as well, consisted of attempts to reproduce mosaics. He had probably seen fine examples of Italian work in this field at the home of Count Vorontsov. Struck by the artistic and delicate work of the Italian artists, Lomonosov resolved to try his own skill at the first opportunity. As basic material he decided to use not natural minerals but artificially prepared opaque glass which, after being cast into little sticks, was polished at one end and then used to compose pictures.

First came the task of preparing glass of this kind. Almost three years of work in the newly constructed chemical laboratory was devoted to it. Each experiment was conducted strictly quantitatively; all the substances used were weighed out exactly and their weights written down precisely, as was the method of melting and the results obtained. One of the laboratory journals has come down to the present time and was deciphered by me not long ago. The entire journal is written in Latin. On the whole more than 3,000 experiments were made with the result that the first problem was solved—Lomonosov could now prepare glass of any shade of color. Later the actual technique of assembling the mosaic pictures was gradually evolved. The pieces of glass, cast in the form of small sticks and polished, were fastened by means of a special cement (mastic) onto a copper pan or tray of the same dimensions the finished picture was to have. When the assembly was finished, the whole picture was polished once more to remove any unevenness and roughness and was placed in a brightly gilded copper frame.

His first work, which was made entirely in the chemical laboratory of the Academy of Sciences and was an image of the Virgin after the painting of the Italian artist Solimena, Lomonosov presented to the Empress Elizabeth on September 4, 1752. The offering was accepted "with pleasure." Lomonosov himself informed the chancellery of the academy of the details of this image: "The total number of component pieces set was more than 4,000, all done by his own hands, and 2,184 experiments in a glass furnace were made to obtain the proper mixtures; and in order that this enterprise should not come to an end at the academy . . . to give him a worthy pupil to teach, since he had invented all the methods for this work which he could sufficiently demonstrate: but he himself could not work at it forever since he wished to serve his fatherland in other branches of knowledge and sciences."

Encouraged by this initial success, he immediately presented two projects to the senate: one was a project for the founding of a mosaic factory to compose pictures, with a yearly maintenance of 3,710 rubles; the other was a plan for a glass factory to manufacture glasses of various colors, glass beads, imitation jet, and other similar things not produced at the time in Russia, but which he estimated could be produced more cheaply than foreign ones. To this end he requested a landed property, not more than 150 versts from Petersburg, with a forest and not less than two hundred

"souls" of peasants (serfs) of the masculine sex; he asked
further that his glass factory be exempted from any kind of
tax or duty for several years, that 4,000 rubles be given for
the construction, which sum would be returned, and the
privilege that for thirty years no similar factory be constructed in Russia.

The senate was sympathetically disposed only to the
second project, and as early as December 14, 1752, it permitted Lomonosov to build the factory he requested under
the proposed conditions, as it would be profitable for the
state. The question of the landed property and the peasant
serfs hung fire since it depended exclusively on the empress.
Lomonosov based all his hopes on the fact that he was
known at court and also enjoyed the patronage of Shuvalov.
At the end of 1752 he wrote him a rhymed letter on the
advantages of glass, *They think falsely, Shuvalov, who
esteem glass less than minerals.*

Time went on and there were no results, but in June 1753
Lomonosov had to give the Department of Manufactures
a report on the status of the factory. Therefore he decided
to travel to Moscow in order to promote the matter personally. It came to pass thus: first of all, Lomonosov presented to the chancellery of the academy a statement asking
that he be given leave for twenty-nine days to go to Moscow
and that a request be sent to the post stage office for horses
and carts. The chancellery refused this, referring to the order
of the president of the academy that no leave was to be
given to academicians without his knowledge during the
time of his stay in Moscow. Then Lomonosov turned to the
senate with the same request. On May 1 they issued an
order in which, having proved first of all their right to grant
leave, they commanded "to release their advisor and professor for a month from this date and to give him a passport
and three post-carts for his trip, for the statutory fare to
be paid with his own money, and in order to make certain

that he would return to the academy on time, to bind him with a formal obligation." Before setting out, Lomonosov drew up a report to the chancellery that in his absence "arrangements in the chemical laboratory had been made so that there should be no pause in the affairs being carried on." He left on the fifth or sixth of March and was in Moscow on the thirteenth. He was well received by Count Razumovsky and obtained everything he sought. He set back on the seventeenth and on the twenty-third of March reported to the chancellery: "Having straightened out the required needs in Moscow, returned and found the laboratory in good condition." For his arbitrary departure he later received a reprimand from the president of the academy, as did the other persons who aided him in it.

According to a decree of Elizabeth on March 16, 1753, Lomonosov received "for work on a factory in the Koporsky district: from the Kovazhsky estate from the village of Shiskin 136, from the village of Kalishch 29, from the village of Ust Ruditsy 12; from the estate of Gorya Valday from the village of Perekuly and Lipovoy 34—in all 212 souls with all the lands belonging to them according to the inventory books." He himself gives the following further details in a letter to L. Euler on February 12, 1754: "9,000 desyatins of land in all—sufficient fields, pastures, fishing streams, many forests, four villages—the nearest eighty-four versts from St. Petersburg, the farthest eighty versts. The land extends to the sea and is irrigated by a small river, where, besides a house and the glass factory which has already been constructed (in Ust Ruditsy) I am erecting a dam, a flour mill, and a saw mill; on it is being put up a self-recording meteorological observatory, which with God's help I shall present to public judgment the coming summer. . . ." The estate of Gorya Valday was called Korovalday in the nineteenth century and up to the revolution belonged to the manufacturer San Galli.

The factory was constructed during the summer of 1753, and skilled workmen of the academy assisted in the building, as is seen in a report of Lomonosov to the chancellery of the academy on September 6: "According to a decree of Her Imperial Highness read and issued by the senate, for the building of a factory for the making of beads and other articles of glass, it is ordered to all whom it may concern to give any assistance which is required. Chemical furnaces are to be set up in the laboratory which has been installed in the above-mentioned factory. These can be set up by none so well as by the furnace builders of the academy, who have built similar furnaces in the laboratory of the academy under my direction and already know the methods necessary therefor through my demonstration. For that reason let Princess A. N. grant leave to one of these stove makers to come to my factory for six weeks, and in his stead for the ordinary work of the academy to order an outsider to be hired at my expense. _____ day of September, 1753."

This was done at once. Later, in May 1754, he ordered from the instrument room a lathe to be used in the production of the many colored glasses and pearls, strings of beads, glass jet, and all sorts of fancy articles and decorations made of them. The machine was ready on December 13. A second machine of the same kind was ordered a year later, in December 1755. In May 1754 a copper plate and lead cylinder were made.

In all probability Lomonosov's factory in Ust Ruditsy was at that time already equipped and adapted to its purpose, for on January 4, 1755, he wrote to Shuvalov: "With this have come to an end all of my great chemical labors, which I have carried on for three years and which it would be unbearable torture for me to lose fruitlessly. . . ."

Lomonosov's glass factory at Ust Ruditsy consisted of a main building, eight by six sazhens in size and equipped with numerous furnaces, which was a laboratory for the manufacture of all possible kinds of glass. Attached to it was a workshop six by four sazhens in size. The water mill about which Lomonosov writes supplied power not only for two sawmills and one grain-crushing millstone but also for the stampers which ground the raw materials for making glass. Also the glass products were polished at the mill. In this way he introduced the mechanization of work to an important degree. Not long ago, I. I. Sidorov studied this history of the Lomonosov factory. He points out that Lomonosov himself, who had no models to guide him, invented machines to prepare the glass beads and jet which he constantly improved, devised all necessary tools, and managed the installation of the furnaces. The workers were peasants of his villages; again it was he who trained them, sometimes sending them to the workshops of the academy. Along with the technical preparations, Lomonosov also evolved an assortment of products which was most remarkable. In addition to the articles already mentioned, he made decanters, plates, spitoons, saucers, wine glasses, paper weights, studs, snuff boxes, cane heads, cast tiles, varicolored glass utensils, and other objects. In general this was an enterprise of industrial art.

Though he had successfully solved the organizational and technical problems, Lomonosov did not master the financial side of the business. The development of a demand required time, and he did not have sufficient means to await this development. He was unable to repay the loan from the state treasury since the factory demanded constant expenditures, and there were almost no profits. Therefore he turned to mosaics in the hope of averting the financial ruin of his factory by obtaining orders for mosaic portraits from the crown. The last ten years of his life were very difficult ones for him, overclouded with constant care concerning money matters. He was most unwilling to give up his factory, his dearest child, the realization of the labors of many years,

but it swallowed up all his means and constantly demanded
new expenditures.

During 1753 and 1754 the work on mosaics continued in
the laboratory of the academy, where pupils worked under
Lomonosov's direction and where he himself probably
worked as well. The mosaics produced there, as is evident in
many documents, were such as we see described in a letter
to Count Peter Ivanovich Shuvalov dated May 10, 1753:
"A testimonial commensurate with my sincere zeal I made
so bold as to show to your very dear spouse, Lady Mavra
Yegorovna, and with it a little example of the mosaic art
which is just beginning in Russia. This specimen has striking imperfections but, because of the novelty of the work
and the smallness of the picture, I trust it may obtain some
excuse for me; and especially if it be placed somewhat higher
in a suitable position."

Lomonosov then turned his chief attention to the mosaic
portrait of Peter I, which was produced in the Bonovsky
house out of smalt prepared in the chemical laboratory of
the academy. And in the journals of the chancellery for
1753 and 1754 we come upon numerous demands for coal
required for production of the glass of this portrait and for
advances of money to buy materials. The portrait was not
finished until 1755, when it was presented to the senate. In
the journal of the senate on December 12, 1755, it is noted
that "Professor Lomonosov was admitted and reported to
the assembly of the ruling senate that, in token of gratitude
for the glass-bead factory provided for him, he had made
out of mosaic stones a portrait of the blessed and worthy of
the memory of eternal glory, the Sovereign Emperor Peter
the Great. After announcing this, he requested that this
portrait should be accepted from him by the ruling senate.
It was then ordered: that this portrait made by the said
Councillor Lomonosov should be accepted by the ruling
senate, which was thereupon done, and that he, Lomonosov,

should be informed by the assembly of the ruling senate that the senate was pleased with such employment of his labors."

Let us now note briefly the further development of Lomonosov's mosaic work. After 1755 the smalt was no longer prepared in the academy laboratory but in his own factory. He did not cease to turn to various personages for orders; however, these were not forthcoming. Only I. I. Shuvalov in 1757 wanted a portrait to be made—probably of the empress, according to letters to him from Lomonosov. In October 1757 Lomonosov submitted a petition to the senate addressed to Elizabeth in which, pointing out that he had achieved perfection in the art of mosaics, he asked that orders be given to him for suitable pictures "for the beautification of public buildings, made according to given originals or drawings, at a suitable price." On October 16, 1757, the senate ordered that this petition be referred to the chancellery of the Academy of Sciences in order to "examine this work in mosaics, inspect it, and present a report to the ruling senate." The examination was carried on in the assembly of the Academy of Arts, which found the colors of the smalt good and the mosaic work solid and equal in perfection to the very best mosaic work in Italy (November 4, 1757). The senate then sent out edicts to the Chancellery for Building and to other places "where public buildings with ornamentation are being constructed, that he, Lomonosov, be called upon to adorn them where necessary with mosaics, for a suitable price; and to give him originals or drawings for the composition of the necessary objects" (February 11, 1757). And at that same time (February 20) Count P. I. Shuvalov proposed to make mosaic pictures in the church situated inside the Saint Petersburg fortress, and also to use them in decorating the monument to Peter the Great which was then being projected. Suitable projects and estimates were drawn up by Lomonosov, together with

The museum and library of the Academy of Sciences

The library of the Academy of Sciences

Stählin and others, and submitted on March 30. However, further progress in the matter was for some reason delayed, and for more than a year Lomonosov impatiently awaited its solution. Just at this time Tredyakovsky inserted in the *Industrious Bee,* a journal of the day, a short note on mosaics in which he advanced the idea that painting with a brush is much finer than pictures in mosaics since it is impossible to produce all of the beauty of a good picture with stones and glass. In this utterly harmless little article Lomonosov saw an ominous conspiracy against his mosaic pictures. He wrote very heatedly about it to I. I. Shuvalov and begged him to show the utmost cooperation in order to secure the earliest possible confirmation of the report on the decoration of the Cathedral of SS. Peter and Paul.

It was not until November 1760 that Elizabeth, who expressed her favor in principle to the construction of a monument with mosaics, proposed that the opinions of scholars and artistic persons be asked as to what kind of mausoleum-monument to Peter I should be erected. On July 6, 1761, the senate ordered Lomonosov to present estimates for the mosaic pictures for this monument and ordered Shuvalov to present sketches of these pictures either to the Rome or the Paris academy, or to the local academy, for examination. The estimate was presented after it had been lowered almost by half from the initial 148,682 rubles to only 80,764. On March 29 of that year Lomonosov received 6,000 rubles on account, and the balance at the rate of 13,460 rubles a year.

From this money he repaid the first loan of 4,000 rubles which had been made to build the glass factory, and began to equip a workshop for setting mosaic pictures on his own land behind his house on Novoisaakiyevsky Street. Here too were built ten rooms (also of stone) for the craftsmen. The first picture was *The Battle of Poltava,* begun in the same year, 1761. When it approached completion, Catherine II on June 7, 1764, visited Lomonosov in his home and examined the picture with care; in all she spent about two hours at Lomonosov's house.

In a few days the picture was finished. It was twelve arshins wide, eleven arshins high, and was set in a flat copper pan weighing eighty poods, reinforced with iron strips weighing more than fifty poods. It was placed on a special timber frame so that it could easily be brought into any desired position and turned about at will. The original of the work was apparently made by Lomonosov himself and his student artists. It has nothing in common with the picture of P. D. Martaine the younger, which is often pointed out as having served Lomonosov for a model. This picture is in the palace of Catherine at Pushkin [Tsarskoye Selo].

What is left of Lomonosov's picture can be seen in the Academy of Sciences on the grand staircase leading to the great conference chamber (Leningrad, Vasilyevski Ostrov, University Quay 5); a sizable part of the top has been lopped off. Here is Lomonosov's description of *The Battle of Poltava.*

"1. In the foreground is depicted Peter the Great mounted on a powerful horse, his face in half-profile; the figure is drawn from a plaster head, poured into a mold taken from the face itself, and with colors copied from the best portraits accessible for examination in Petersburg. The seated figure is a sazhen high and all else is in proportion.

"2. Behind the ruler are the most important generals of the time—Sheremetev, Menshikov, Golitsyn—whose portraits are taken from existing originals.

"3. Peter the Great is represented to be in considerable danger as he last rode forth to combat when Charles the Twelfth was turning in retreat; before and behind him the generals and soldiers, who are protecting the sovereign, are shooting and bayoneting the enemy soldiers.

"4. Nearby in the foreground is a grenadier with a bayonet directed at an enemy, looking around at the monarch as if indignant that he should expose himself to such great danger.

"5. Behind lie a heap of casualties: a Swedish cannon with a shattered carriage, a horse, and a dead Swede, all visible tokens of a conquered enemy.

"6. Deeper in the picture, behind the attending generals, can be seen banners, trumpets, kettledrummers, and the standards of the Russian regiments.

"7. Farther from the front, toward the middle, are depicted the corpses of vanquished enemies; the Swedes are still defending themselves from the advancing Russians, and violent heavy shooting produces great smoke; near it are visible the redoubts taken by the Swedes at the beginning of the conflict and the bodies of Russians and Swedes.

"8. Even farther from the foreground is represented a captured Swedish general, whom the surrounding Russian soldiers are lifting up; he is weak and dejected.

"9. At some distance Charles the Twelfth is depicted in a simple calash; around him are halberdiers, some of whom, turning the calash about, are urging him to save himself by flight, but he, holding a pistol in his hand before him, is still eager for battle; before him a desperate struggle is going on between the Russians and the Swedish pike men.

"10. The city of Poltava is represented on the horizon with smoke from the cannon fire.

"11. On the right hand are the fleeing Swedish regiments and the pursuing Russians, and on the left a Russian retrenchment and regiments which have marched forth from it but are not yet in combat.

"12. Above the picture is the Holy Apostle Paul at a writing table with a pen in one hand, while with the other hand and with his face he makes a sign of reverence and gratitude. Beneath him on a metal frontlet are written his words from the epistle which was read for the victory of Poltava: 'If God is with us, who can be against us?' "

The second picture, *The Taking of Azov*, was barely begun when Lomonosov died on April 4, 1765. He left a petition in rough draft to the senate asking that in case of his death the project which he had begun be continued and his brother-in-law, Ivan Zilch, be placed at the head of it. "All the colors can be manufactured without me, since for three years now I have taken no part in the composition of these mosaic colors, but my brother-in-law has produced them all . . . workers and students whom I have taught are capable, under the supervision of a good painter, of executing the composition of mosaic pictures after good originals. As for the great pans, their strengthening, arrangement, movement, polishing, and other matters, such as how to bring the picture to perfection and completion—all this the oldest mosaic worker, Matvey Vasilyev, will perform to perfection, since he has worked at this business with me from the very beginning of the mosaic process."

After Lomonosov's death the workshop was moved out of his home and transferred to the home of Ivan Ivanovich Betsky, but soon the best craftsmen, Ivan Zilch and Matvey Vasilyev, left and the business came to an end in 1767. In this year the glass factory in Ust Ruditsy was also closed. In all, twelve mosaic pictures are known to have been made in Lomonosov's workshop. Three of them were completed after his death and five of them are attributed to Lomonosov himself. But on the basis of data which have been preserved the total number of pictures issued from his workshop must be considerably greater.

After him, the art of mosaics ceased among us for a long time. I may add that in May 1764 Lomonosov was chosen an honorary member of the Academy of Science of Bologna for his merit in mosaic art. Earlier that year in the learned journal *Florentine News* of March 12, 1764, there appeared an article describing Lomonosov's contributions to the production of colored glass and mosaics.[3]

The mosaic business, like his glass factory, brought only losses to Lomonosov, and all his hopes of straightening out his affairs came to naught. He fell deeper and deeper into debt, and among his papers are preserved notes addressed to other academicians on this score—requests to extend the expiration dates of loans. What deep meaning lies in a short poem written by Lomonosov at the time of one of his trips from St. Petersburg to his factory at Korovalday in 1761:

> Dear Grasshopper, how Fortune doth thee bless,
> Far more than men art granted happiness. . . .
>
> Freely thou speakest and singest, and knowest no care;
> All that thou seest is thine; thy home is everywhere,
> Thou askest for nothing, and thou owest to none.

It should be added, however, that the glass factory business which Lomonosov instituted did not completely perish. In 1752 the state glass factory turned to Lomonosov with the request that one of the students, Peter Druzhinin, be taught the art of making colored crystal. Lomonosov taught him for one year and at the end of the instruction gave him the formulas for the preparation of colored glasses. Druzhinin then applied these formulas in the factory and the preparation of colored crystal, under his leadership, became firmly established there. The artistic handiwork of the glass factory was esteemed very highly throughout the nineteenth century and is still produced today; in it survive the modest labors of Lomonosov carried out in the tiny chemical laboratory of the Academy of Sciences, "between walls and by the fire."

We may add to this still another province of chemical

[3] Those interested in further details of Lomonosov's mosaic venture will find them in the book of N. Makarenko and in the articles of N. I. Sidorov.

technology in which Lomonosov worked—namely, the preparation of porcelain. The experiments necessary to obtain this product, as notes which have been preserved reveal, were made in 1751 and 1752. The records of seven series of experiments remain—probably by no means all there were. Lomonosov himself writes thus of his work in this field:[4] "Under the observation and according to the instructions of Lomonosov a chemical laboratory was erected in which he, laboring in many experiments along with other researches, invented the substance of porcelain." His formulas were later applied in a porcelain factory.[5]

[4] In *A Short History of the Conduct of the Chancellery of the Academy* . . . (1764).

[5] Lomonosov could not have "invented" porcelain. Rather, he must have devised a formula for an imitation of Chinese porcelain, an activity which had engaged alchemists and potters in Europe since the sixteenth century. Many factories had been established throughout Europe, notably in France and Germany, before Lomonosov's discovery. Perhaps the most famous and successful was Meissen porcelain, developed by Johann Friedrich Böttger in 1709 after he discovered the secret of kaolin. In fact, "at Saint Petersburg, Russia, about 1745, Empress Elizabeth started a hard-paste factory which has continued to this day. The chief work strongly imitates Meissen (Dresden) during the Seven Years' War period as the workmen were from Meissen. . . ." (See PORCELAIN, *The Encyclopedia Americana*.) ED.

CHAPTER 5

Peculiarities of the art of chemistry in the beginning of the eighteenth century—The chemical "individuum" and quantitative determinations—Chemistry, a science—Chemistry according to Lomonosov—Chemical elements and phlogiston—The academic theory in chemistry—Speech about the benefits of chemistry—The law of the conservation of the weight of matter in chemical reaction—Fire, burning, and calcination of metals—The experiments of Boyle, Lomonosov, and Lavoisier—Physical chemistry and apparatus for it—Lectures and physico-chemical experiments—Lomonosov as a teacher—The significance of physical chemistry—The study of the primordial particles.

As WE PROCEED to a survey of Lomonosov's activity in the field of his profession, chemistry, we must first of all acquaint ourselves in more detail with the status of that science in his day and supplement what was said in Chapter 2 about his study of the subject at Marburg. The inductive method of investigation, which made experiment the touchstone of all propositions and hypotheses and had already begun to be applied generally to the natural sciences early in the sixteenth century, influenced chemistry comparatively little even in the eighteenth century. This was the result of a series of historical causes. First, it must be borne in mind that for long centuries there had been not "chemistry" but "alchemy." All operations of the "alchemists" were carried on in strict secrecy. If ever made public they were, for the most part, expressed in such allegorical language that only those initiated into the cryptic meanings of one author or another could understand anything in the books on alchemy. The goals of the chemical experimenters of that time were to turn base metals into gold, to obtain the elixir of life, and so on, which also tended strongly to shroud their operations in mystery.

Those who in the Middle Ages worked in applied chemistry, and also with chemical processes of various kinds, quite understandably did not make their methods and formulas public property but passed them on carefully from generation to generation, just as at the present time many chemical manufacturing processes are kept secret so that, if a given process is to be learned, it must be subjected to thorough study in the laboratory and in the pilot plant. Such was the case, for instance, from 1914 to 1918 during the World War, when it was found necessary to introduce with urgent speed in England, France, and the United States many chemical processes that had hitherto been monopolies of Germany.

An important reason why experimentation did not play the role it should have in the chemistry of the time is to be found furthermore in the lack, even in the middle of the eighteenth century, of the concept of the so-called "chemical individuum," that is, a "chemically pure" or homogeneous substance (element or compound) which does not contain any admixture of other substances. It is quite evident that one and the same result in one and the same experiment may be obtained by different experimenters when they work with one and the same substance. But this in turn is realizable only on condition that all the investigators are dealing with chemically pure substances, "chemical individua," and that the same name on their phials stands for the same contents.

Today, now that the importance of the concept of the chemical individuum has long been understood and means have been worked out which enable us to control rigidly the identity of each chemical substance, we can reproduce any experiment, regardless of who may have described it, with the confidence that we shall obtain thereby exactly the same results as the author himself. This was not the case in Lomonosov's time. Although the chemists no longer concealed their work and there were already a goodly number of printed guides to chemistry with detailed descriptions of chemical substances and various chemical experiments, still the description of those substances are usually nebulous in the extreme. They were not yet able to characterize them by their physical and chemical properties as we do now. Experiments all too often produced different results in the hands of different chemists because the substances of identical name at their disposal really represented different mixtures of several chemical substances.

Unquestionably this lack of comprehension of the chemical individuum was in its turn the result of the methods of investigation applied at the time. According to a definition by chemical authorities of the first half of the eighteenth century, chemistry was the art of analyzing complex substances into their component parts and, in reverse, of compounding complex substances of the latter. And this definition was completely right. Chemistry then consisted of just that. Gradually, as methods were multiplied and perfected, the art of analyzing substances made unquestionable progress. But it was still considered quite sufficient simply to analyze a substance into its component parts. Definition of the proportions, by weight, in which those component parts existed in the initial substance—what we now call quantitative determination—was not considered necessary. However, the history of chemistry shows that real progress began only after such quantitative methods were introduced. Scales and other exact physical apparatus became indispensable equipment for the chemist of the nineteenth century, and only with their help did the possibility of discovering chemical laws become manifest.

Chemistry in Lomonosov's time was an art, not a science. The first presumes only the ability to perform analyses and an acquaintance with those operations which make it possible to achieve them. In this is the crux of the chemistry of the period. Then, there were long, disconnected, and unrelated descriptions of substances obtained from animals, minerals, and vegetables which were in the great majority of cases accidental, sometimes very complex, mixtures of individual chemical compounds. For example, the chemistry presented in the two huge volumes of Boerhaave, which Lomonosov studied, was presented according to such a plan. Science does not consist of a chaotic collection of facts; it should primarily be occupied with a systematization of the facts which belong to its province, together with their classification from some general point of view; only when this has been done do we have science before us. By the very nature of things these classifications change with the course of time; with the accumulation of knowledge and the rise of new points of view, a new more complete system supplants the old. Thus it was correct to characterize chemistry in the beginning of the eighteenth century not as a science but as an art. It was just this period in which the first attempt that was made to bring all chemical data into relation with one hypothesis belongs. This was the attempt to bring the data into a system with the help of the theory of phlogiston, which was discussed in Chapter 2.

Lomonosov stands far in advance of his contemporaries in his attitude toward chemistry and toward the lines along which its development and transformation into a genuine science had to proceed. First of all, we find in him a clear concept of the chemical "individual entity," the chemically pure substance, as being indispensable in order to obtain uniform results in repeated experiments. In his project for the founding of a chemical laboratory (March 1745) he states what he intends to do in the laboratory as follows:

"First, to purify with every kind of endeavor the necessary natural materials utilized in chemical work so that there shall be no kind of foreign admixture which might cause deception in other reactions; second, to split up the purified materials so far as possible into those of which they are naturally composed; third, to prove better that the substances which have been thus divided consist of those simple ones, I intend to reunite them as far as possible."

Further on in the same project he points out in detail the necessity for quantitative investigation: "In all the experiments I have mentioned I shall note and record not only the reactions themselves and the weight or measure of the materials or vessels employed, but also the circumstances which will necessarily be manifest." Then we find everywhere detailed indication of the necessity of applying the methods of physics to chemical investigation, and, indeed, Lomonosov himself always performed all his chemical work with the help of balances and other physical instruments which made it possible to make exact measurements.

In complete conformity with this basic program is the definition of chemistry which we find in Lomonosov's first chemical work, *The Principles of Mathematical Chemistry* (1741): "Chemistry is the science of the changes occurring in a complex substance to the extent that it is complex." This definition is very close to the contemporary definition of chemistry, and here for the first time chemistry is called a *science*. In 1741 Lomonosov conceived of this science as one of chemical facts unified by the mathematical method of exposition and incorporated into a system based upon the atomic theory; in consequence, as we shall see, according to his opinion physics too should serve as a means for defining and unifying chemical data.

Then we find in the above-mentioned *Principles of Mathematical Chemistry* a complete and clearly expressed concept of the basic unit of matter in chemistry—the chemical element as the "simple" body, the original substance which cannot be analyzed into simpler substances, and of which all complex substances consist. "A complex substance consists of two or more different basic substances so combined among themselves that in each of its corpuscles there is just the same interrelation of the elements which make up the substance as there is between the separate elements in every complex substance." However, this view had no influence whatsoever on the history of chemistry: *The Principles of Mathematical Chemistry* remained unfinished and never saw the light.

Lomonosov's basic substance is the chemical element, as characterized by Robert Boyle in 1661—a simple substance not capable of further division by chemical analysis. This conception gained ground with chemists little by little during the eighteenth century until, after several decades, Lavoisier made it the foundation of his doctrine of the chemical elements. What Lomonosov says further about "elements" and "corpuscles" is extremely interesting; elements are in essence the atoms of the chemists, whereas corpuscles are the molecules. Here we have the first combination, the first unification of two conceptions of the elements, both of which date from remote antiquity: one speaks of elements as qualities, and according to the other atoms are elements, the very small elementary particles of all substances incapable of being further divided.

Lomonosov brought about the unification of these two points of view and introduced as a basic proposition the concept of the corpuscle-molecule having exactly the same quantitative composition as the entire body of which it is a part. In this respect Lomonosov's theory approximated Dalton's, which called the corpuscle or molecule of a complex substance a complex atom. But, as a predecessor of Dalton, Lomonosov did not have at his disposal those exact quantitative facts which Dalton possessed, facts which were a result of the development of quantitative chemical analysis in the last quarter of the eighteenth century. And without those quantitative facts it was impossible to work out the chemical atomic theory since they alone gave it the necessary point of support.

Lomonosov, following the chemists of his time, recognized immaterial, imponderable element-qualities along with the material elements not susceptible of decomposition by analysis: i.e. mercury (the principle of volatility), salt (the principle of constancy, unchanged by roasting), and sulphur (the principle of combustibility, called at that time phlogiston). With the help of this latter element-quality Ernst Stahl and his followers first combined the phenomenon of burning and the phenomenon of roasting metals, and later other chemical phenomena; Lomonosov, unlike other chemists, never considered phlogiston a substance having a negative weight (that is, decreasing the weight of the substance with which it was combined) and being capable of passing through all substances, and possessing other curious properties. He always laughed at such theories.

A distinguishing feature of Lomonosov's chemistry was its close connection with his atomic theory, on which, as we have seen, all his physics was based. He considered absolutely indispensable in chemistry (as well as in physics) a preliminary acquaintance with those elementary particles which form all substances and from whose properties the chemical properties of substances also proceed. He expresses his views excellently in a *Speech on the Uses of Chemistry, delivered on September 6 of the year* 1751. Here are a few excerpts from it:

"When we examine natural objects we find in them properties of a twofold nature. Some we understand clearly and in detail; the others, although we conceive of them clearly in our mind, we are not able to portray in detail. To the first type belong size, appearance, motion, and the position of the whole object; to the second, color, taste, smell, medicinal virtue, and others. We can measure the first exactly through Geometry and can define them by means of Mechanics; with the second it is impossible to apply such detail since the first have their basis in visible and tangible substances, while the others have theirs in the most delicate particles, far removed from our senses. But to gain an exact and detailed knowledge of an object one must know the parts which constitute it. . . . In the same way it is impossible to have a detailed understanding of the above-mentioned qualities of the second type without having investigated the most minute and indivisible particles from which they proceed, an understanding of which is as necessary for the investigator of Nature as these very particles are indispensable to the structure of substances. And although in present times the microscopes which have been invented have so enlarged the power of our vision that in a barely visible grain of dust it is possible to distinguish clearly a great number of particles, yet these useful instruments serve only to investigate organic parts, such as the little bladders and ducts forming the solid parts of animal and vegetable organs, which are very delicate and invisible to the naked eye. But the microscopes are unable to make visible those particles which make up mixed matter. For example, through Chemistry it is known, for instance, that there is mercury in cinnabar and pipe clay [terra alba] in alum; but it is impossible to distinguish either the mercury in the cinnabar or the pipe clay in the alum by means of the very best microscopes since both always have the same appearance. Only through Chemistry can one acquire a true conception of them. Here I see, you say, that Chemistry only shows the matter of which compound substances are made up and not each individual particle of them. To this I answer that, in truth, in these times the sharp eye of the investigator cannot penetrate so far into the interior of substances; but if at some future time this secret shall be revealed, then truly Chemistry will be the leader, the first to draw the curtain from this inner sanctuary of Nature. . . .

"The zealous lover of Nature's beauties who wishes to explore the deeply hidden state of the elementary particles which constitute substances ought to examine all those properties and changes—and especially those revealed by Chemistry, her closest servant and confidante, who has access to her innermost chambers. When she combines particles that are divided and dispersed in solution into solid fragments and shows their different [crystalline] forms, she asks advice of cautious and sagacious Geometry. When she changes solid substances into liquids and liquids into solids, and combines and divides matter of different types, she takes counsel with exact and ingenious Mechanics. And when she produces various colors through the fusion of liquid materials, she investigates them through penetrating Optics. In this manner, when Chemistry sorts out the very rich and secret treasures of her mistress, and the curious and indefatigable zealot of Nature begins to measure them through Geometry, to weigh them by Mechanics, and to observe them through Optics;—then it is extremely probable that he will penetrate the mysteries as he desires. . . .

"Eyes are useless to the man who wishes to see the interior of an object yet lacks a hand to open it. Hands are useless to the man who has no eyes to observe the objects once they have been disclosed. Chemistry may correctly be called the hands, and Mathematics the eyes of Physics. But as surely as each demands aid from the other, just as surely, notwithstanding, they often divert human minds into different paths. The Chemist, who sees in every experiment different and frequently unexpected phenomena and products and is thereby allured to gain a speedy advantage, laughs at the Mathematician as being involved only in certain vain cogitations about points and lines. The Mathe-

matician, on the other hand, convinced of his propositions
by exact proofs and evolving unknown properties of quantities through incontestable and uninterrupted deductions,
scorns the Chemist as occupied only with practice and lost
in many chaotic experiments; being himself accustomed to
clean paper and shining geometric instruments, he abhors
the smoke and dust of Chemistry. And thus up to this time
these two sisters, closely associated for the common good,
have for the most part given birth to sons of such different
opinions. This is the reason why the complete study of
Chemistry has not yet been combined with a profound
knowledge of Mathematics."

We shall return again to the thoughts expressed here
since Lomonosov developed them widely in the following
years and they were eventually cast into a new chemical
discipline—physical chemistry.

At the present time we regard the law of the conservation
of matter as the foundation of all chemical changes. This
law states that the total weight of the chemical substances
entering into a reaction is equal to the total weight of the
new chemical substances formed by this reaction. The idea
that matter generally can neither disappear nor create itself,
that the quantity of it in the universe remains constant, had
been expressed long since and applied by the philosophers
of the seventeenth and eighteenth centuries as a self-evident
proposition which did not require any proofs whatsoever.
We sometimes find that proposition among the writings of
chemists of this period—for instance, in one of Robert
Boyle's works—but no one until Lomonosov considered it
the all-important law which lies at the foundation of the
entire edifice of chemistry. Failure to do so was evidently
due to the fact that the quantitative method was not applied in chemical investigations, as we have already pointed
out, because of the absence of recorded chemical experiments analogous to those performed by the noted J. B. van

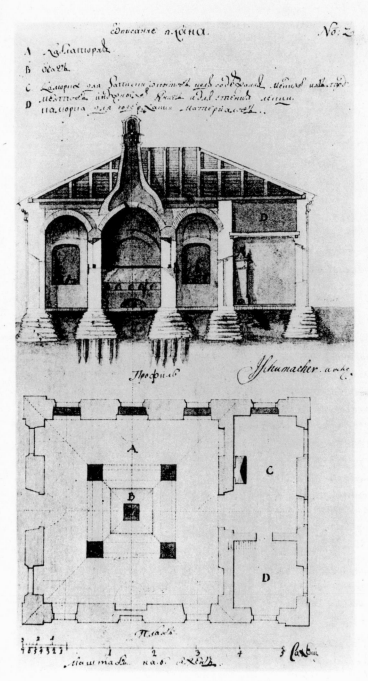

Plan and elevation of Lomonosov's laboratory

Primus Vera Chymica
PROLEGOMENA Physica

Caput primum.
de Chymia Physica ejusque officia.

§. 1.

Chymia Physica est scientia ~~explicans~~ ~~...~~ expriendorum et experimentorum
~~...~~ ~~...~~ ~~...~~ ~~...~~ ~~...~~ per qui in corporibus
mixtis fiunt per operationes chy-
micas. Potest etiam philosophica
Chymica nominari, ~~...~~

§. 2.

Chymiae Physicae nomine opusculum hoc indigitare
ideo voluimus, quia omnem operam in id solum
conferre apud nos statuimus, ut nil in eo pro-
ponatur, nisi quod ad explicandam modo scienti-
fico mixtronem corporum conducat. Si circa
omnia, quae ad rem oeconomicam, pharma-
ceuticam, metallurgicam, ut traduare etc.
spectant, hinc exclusa ad speciale ~~...~~ tractationes judicamus
chymiae technicae ~~...~~, referenda judicamus
~~...~~, eum in finem, ut 1) quisque scopo suo
convenientes cognitionem facile inveniat, sine
tedio legat. 2) ne tanta rerum varietate discen-
tium animi obruantur. 3) ne philosophicam pul-
cherrimae naturae contemplationellem praeceps
lucri cupido turbet; sed ut potius 4) impressa
animo clara mixtorum notione, studiosus chymiae cultor ad augenda per eam vitae com-
moda oculatus tandem accedat.

§. 3.

Per scientiam definimus chymiam, naturalis phi-
losophiae scriptores imitati; qui cum patiorum

Helmont about 1640. Thus, for instance, he took a quantity of silver which had been weighed out and dissolved it in nitric acid, thus changing it into nitrate of silver; by heating the nitrate of silver red hot he recovered the silver from it, and the weight of the silver recovered was exactly equal to the weight of the silver dissolved in the first place.

We find reflections on this proposition in Lomonosov's early notes, probably borrowed from some work or other. He first expressed these thoughts with full clarity in a letter to the eminent mathematician L. Euler on July 5, 1748, using the identical expressions in which he later (1758) communicated them to the conference of the academy in a dissertation on the relation of the quantity of a substance to its weight, *Observations on the Solid and Liquid States of Substances* (1760). "All changes occurring in Nature are subject to the condition that, if so much is taken away from one substance, just as much is added to another. Thus, if matter decreases somewhat in one place, then it increases in another place. As many hours as a person devotes to wakefulness, just so many he takes away from sleep. This universal natural law extends to the very laws of motion; thus one body, moving another by its own force, loses just so much force as it communicates to the other which receives movement from it."

Evidently Lomonosov did not hasten to publish this law, probably because, on the one hand, he considered it generally known in view of the proposition which had been enunciated long since by philosophers, as pointed out above. On the other hand, for a long time he himself had no clear conception of its importance in chemical changes. It was precisely from 1753 to 1756 that he conducted a series of experiments, about which I shall now speak, that served to convince him of the correctness of the law in its application to the processes of chemistry. It is generally considered that Lavoisier was the first to express this law in 1789, in his chemistry course; but he nowhere called it definitely a law. It is curious that the law of the conservation of matter during chemical reactions was not to be found in textbooks and chemistry manuals until the 1860's, after it had received the most exact experimental verification in the works of J. Stas. A similar verification was made again in the present century in the experiments of H. Landolt in which the law of the conservation of weight was revealed as fully exact within the limits of the precision of weight measurements.

This law is closely connected with one of the questions which especially attracted the attention of chemists of the seventeenth and eighteenth centuries and which were subjects of the research of nearly all of them. That was the question of the nature of fire, of the processes of burning and calcination of metals. Naturally, these processes were fundamental at that time in chemistry since almost the sole active agent in chemical operations was fire in one form or another. Fire, as we have seen, was then still considered by almost everyone to be a basic chemical element. It was true that they could not separate it: however, that did not prevent them from declaring it to be an element. Again, of those chemical changes which were produced with the aid of fire, the phenomenon of the calcination of base metals attracted great attention—in distinction from the precious metals, which are not subject to the action of fire. Here is a simple illustration of the action of fire:

A piece of base metal, such as lead or tin, is heated in air. At first the metals melts, and then little by little changes into a gray substance which, in its external appearance, has nothing in common with the metal. What remains was called, in earlier terminology, "calx" (cinder), in modern nomenclature, "oxide." If one weighs the piece of metal before burning, and then the cinder which is formed from it, it will be found that the latter weighs considerably more than the metal. How explain this fact, which was noted as early as the twelfth century?

Disregarding earlier attempts at explanation, let us begin at the middle of the eighteenth century, when the phenomenon of the burning of metals was usually explained by one or the other of two hypotheses. According to one, the matter of fire passes through the walls of the vessel containing the metal being burned and unites with it. According to the other, every metal consists of cinder and phlogiston: during the burning the phlogiston flies off and the cinder remains. The first hypothesis was thought to be firmly established by the experiments of the famous English chemist Robert Boyle; the second was defended by Ernst Stahl and his followers, among whom were almost all chemists of that time.

Lomonosov, as we already know, was so skeptically disposed toward all of the imponderable substances of his century that he denied their existence. In like manner he did not believe in the matter of fire, and in his *Meditations on the Cause of Heat and Cold* subjected it to such merciless criticism that the members of the conference, on hearing the dissertation, returned it to Lomonosov to tone down the expressions which he used when referring to Robert Boyle. In this same dissertation Lomonosov speaks of the possibility of another explanation of the increase in the weight of metal during calcination—specifically, the uniting of the metal with air, which always surrounds the metal.

But one circumstance argued against such an hypothesis. As we have noted, Boyle supported his hypothesis by an experiment conducted as follows (1673): Boyle took a piece of lead, placed it in a glass retort (a vessel with a long neck pointed downward) hermetically sealed, and weighed it. In this condition he heated it in a fire and the lead turned into cinder; then he opened the retort, whereupon Boyle noted the inrush of air accompanied by a whistling sound—

a sign that the vessel had been hermetically sealed—and weighed it again. An increase in weight was revealed, and in explanation he advanced his hypothesis that the substance of fire was capable of penetrating the glass of the retort and uniting with the metal.

Lomonosov repeated this experiment in 1756. He himself writes about it as follows: "I made experiments in firmly sealed glass vessels in order to find out whether the weight of metals increases by the action of pure heat. I found that the opinion of the famous Robert Boyle is false since, without the admission of the outside air the weight of the burned metal remains the same." Lomonosov ascertained, just as had Boyle, that when such a retort is opened after the experiment, the air enters it. This proved (a) that the addition to the weight of the metal by calcination is occasioned by its combining with the air, and (b) that it is impossible to explain the process of the calcination of metal by the aid of phlogiston since, if the phlogiston left the metal, the sealed retort with the metal should have a different weight after heating. Lomonosov made reports on all of these experiments to the conference of the academy, but because they were not published they remained quite unknown.

Seventeen years later, in 1773, Lavoisier repeated Boyle's experiments, with the same results Lomonosov obtained. But he made a new and very important observation— namely, that only a *part* of the air of the sealed retort united with the metal, and that the increase of the weight of the metal, which had turned into calx, was equal to the decrease in weight of the air in the retort. At the same time part of the metal remained in its free form. Hence Lavoisier drew the conclusion that air is composed of two gases, one of which combines with the metal while the other does not. This conclusion was confirmed in an experiment involving the calcination of mercury in a retort exposed to a definite volume of air contained under a glass bell jar immersed in mercury. After twelve days the calcination was stopped because the volume of air under the bell jar ceased to decrease. The air remaining in the bell did not sustain combustion and a mouse could not live in it, therefore Lavoisier called it "azote" (nitrogen), which in Greek means unsuitable for life. The red calx of mercury which was obtained, under subsequent strong heating, broke down into mercury and the gas which had been absorbed by the mercury out of the air. In this gas a candle burned with a blinding brilliance and a mouse felt exhilarated: this was oxygen. Thus the processes of the calcination of metals were finally explained, and at the same time it was proved that air is not an independent element but contains four-fifths nitrogen and one-fifth oxygen. Furthermore, Lavoisier proved that burning is, in general, a union of the burning or heated substance with the oxygen in the air. It is evident from this how close Lomonosov was to the greatest discoveries of the eighteenth century, which laid the foundation of the new chemistry that did not recognize the substance of phlogiston.

Lomonosov spoke, in his plans for founding a chemical laboratory, of teaching students in it. This was possible only after the laboratory was completed; as we have seen, it contained a small room designed, among other things, for giving lectures. Lomonosov did a great deal of work in the preparation of his chemistry course, which was completely original.

Thus on May 15, 1752, a statement of the conference was received at the chancellery according to which Lomonosov "had submitted in writing to the assembly what chemical lectures he intended to deliver and what experiments he planned to make. In this communication he declared that the following instruments were necessary for his course, namely: (1) wooden balances, (2) instruments to study the hardness of solids by pressure and breaking, (3) a grindstone, (4) an instrument to investigate the viscosity of liquid

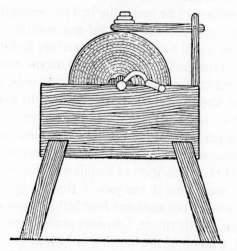

Lomonosov's apparatus for determining
the hardness of substances.

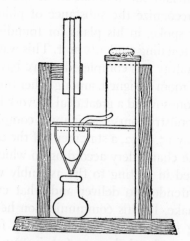

Lomonosov's apparatus for
determining the viscosity of
liquids.

materials according to the number of drops, (5) a Papin machine, (6) a mill with which to grind various materials, (7) a pyrometer, (8) ten simple mercury thermometers. And since the gentlemen in session have approved his intention and have adjudged that the instruments enumerated are very necessary for the project in hand as well as for general use, therefore, it was resolved to report this to the chancellery of the Academy of Sciences in order that these instruments should be made and prepared under the supervision of Councillor Lomonosov for the benefit of the academy in general. And he has attached hereto drawings num-

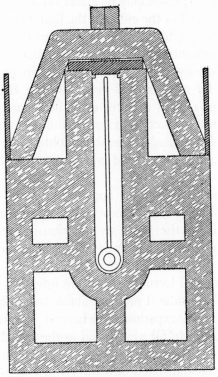

Papin machine, improved by
Lomonosov.

bered one to seven of the designated instruments (except the pyrometer and the thermometers)." Of these seven drawings I have found three in Book 165 of the archives of the Academy of Sciences, which are here reproduced. Drawing 3 (p. 122) represents a grindstone 1.5 feet in diameter used to study the hardness of stones and glass specimens which were clutched in a lateral wooden arm. Drawing 4 (p. 122) is an instrument to determine the viscosity of liquids by the number of drops (per unit of time); it consists of a funnel which is filled with liquid from the reservoir (upper right) always at the same level; in the funnel is placed a sphere (presumably of glass) on a long leg which regulates the speed of the efflux of the liquid by its constant position. According to the number of drops falling from the funnel in a given interval of time one can draw a conclusion about the viscosity of the liquid. Apparatus of this type, perfected to be sure, is used even now for this purpose. Drawing 5 (p. 123) is a Papin machine, "put in the best condition," in cross section. This machine, of massive construction, evidently made it possible to obtain comparatively high pressures. It was ordered and built at the Sestroretsk factories.

The purposes which these apparatus were to serve was stated as follows by Lomonosov in his report, in Latin, to the conference of the Academy of Sciences, delivered on May 11 of the same year, four days before the order for the apparatus:

"In my chemical lectures, which are intended for youthful students, I consider it most profitable to combine physical with chemical experiments wherever possible, and I shall try myself to fulfill what I said in the speech in praise of chemistry at the preceding public session, which I communicate to you translated into the Latin language by the student Yaremsky (this is the *Oration on the Use of Chemistry*). Therefore, in the entire course in experimental chemistry which has been compiled by my labors it is necessary to (1) define the specific gravity of chemical substances, (2) investigate the connection between their particles: (a) by means of the fracture of substances, (b) by compression, (c) by sharpening on a whetstone, and (d) by counting the number of drops of a liquid (per unit of time); (3) to describe the figures of crystallized substance, (4) to subject substances to the action of the Papin machine, (5) to observe the degrees of heat everywhere, (6) to investigate substances, especially metals, by long continued abrasion. In a word, to explore everything that it is possible to measure, weigh, and define by calculation" (*Archives of the Academy of Sciences*, Deposit 1, list 3, p. 239).

Among other apparatus used by Lomonosov in 1752 mention should be made of the machine to study the refraction of rays of light in different liquids. In addition on April 7 he wrote to the chancellery: "If we are to increase manual labor in the chemical laboratory, and especially, in order to demonstrate chemical experiments to the students, it is impossible to get along with one laborer, since there is no less work here than in the botanical garden—such as: carrying wood and coal and putting it in the stoves, washing and cleaning vessels, preparing, grinding, and crushing materials, and keeping the whole laboratory in cleanliness . . . for this let the chancellery of the Academy of Sciences deign to appoint one more furnace-tender for the above-mentioned laboratory." This request was immediately granted.

Thus very fundamental preparatory work was carried on for the presentation of the lectures. And auditors were found, as the following indicates: "Petition of the students Mikhail Sofronov, Ivan Fedorovsky, and Vasily Klementyev. Since chemistry is a science useful in our state, and we too wish to study it, therefore, we most humbly request of the chancellery of the Academy of Sciences that it grant that we go to the professor of that science, His Honor Professor

Lomonosov, who promises to show us experiments and to begin his lectures. With regard to the lectures which we are attending at the present time, we will continue to attend them as we have been until the general assignment by all sciences ensues. February 15, 1750."

Precisely when the lectures themselves began is not known. On the one hand, in May 1752, as is evident from the data cited, Lomonosov was still preparing to begin them; on the other hand, in a report on his activities for September 3, 1752, he writes: "I read chemistry lectures to the students illustrated by chemical experiments, of which even more could be added if only the instruments we ordered would arrive . . . and in the present January third (that is of 1753) I intend to continue chemical experimental lectures to the students." Thus we may probably presume that the lectures began in the summer of 1752. It is possible that their beginning coincided with the opening of the new academic year on July 11. Enumerating his activities in 1752, Lomonosov says: "I performed for the students chemical experiments according to the course which I myself studied under Henckel. For a clear comprehension and a brief notion of chemistry as a whole, I dictated and explained to the students those introductions to physical chemistry in the Latin language which I myself composed, and which are contained on thirteen sheets in 150 paragraphs, together with many drawings on six half-sheets." He says in another place: "I dictated to my students the primary fundamentals of physical chemistry and read lectures on them four hours a week, meanwhile demonstrating physical experiments, to which I could add even more if I could get the required instruments in time."

The lectures continued on into 1753. We know about them from a report submitted by Lomonosov to the chancellery of the Academy of Sciences on February 5, 1753, from which the following extracts are taken:

"In the past year, 1751, on the date of August 30, the students entrusted to me by the order of his excellency the president of the Academy of Sciences—for instruction in poetry, Nikolay Popovsky, and in chemistry, Vasily Klementyev, Ivan Bratkovsky, Ivan Fedorovsky—have made the following progress in their studies. . . . As for my lectures in chemistry, they should be finished about the month of May of this year, 1753, and when they are terminated, the progress of each student will be manifest. In the meantime I am able to testify that Stepan Rumovsky was more able than the others at answering the questions I posed in the lectures, and he attends my lectures diligently with the other students according to the sanction of the chancellery. Ivan Bratkovsky could have a like success if he were not frequently absent from the lectures. Vasily Klementyev is the most diligent of all and, as I observe by the circumstances, understands and remembers fairly well; however, he is extremely bashful in answering my questions so that he is often unable to say what he certainly must know. In Ivan Fedorovsky, although he has good comprehension of the subject, I have observed no great interest in chemistry. [Signed] The Collegiate Councillor and Professor Lomonosov."

The lectures on physical chemistry, as Lomonosov had planned, were finished in May 1753; in an account of his labors for 1753 he remarks that "at the termination of the lectures I performed new physicochemical experiments." With this first and last course of lectures on physical chemistry, so far as we are able to judge, his activity as a university professor came to an end.

This course of Lomonosov, just as he prepared it, is now in the archives of the Academy of Sciences, as is the conspectus dictated to the students which was taken from the notes of Klementyev. I first published the course in translation in 1904. It is extraordinary in its conception. Here are embodied those thoughts which had been already expressed in the *Speech on the Use of Chemistry*, but the chief attention was focused on the union of chemistry with physics. Chemistry itself is defined thus in the first paragraph: "Physical chemistry is the science which explains on the basis of physical propositions and experiments the cause of what takes place through chemical operations in compound substances. It might be called a chemical philosophy, but in a completely different sense than that mystic philosophy in which they not only fail to give explanations but also even carry on the operations themselves in a secret manner." Paragraph 2: "We have called this labor physical chemistry because we have decided to include in it only a scientific explanation of the composition of substances." The fundamental idea embodied in physical chemistry is the study of chemistry by the aid of physics and in the unification of all chemical facts on the ground of physics.

After the termination of the lectures, the students, under Lomonosov's direction, entered upon physicochemical experiments in the laboratory in order to become acquainted through their own experience with what they had completed theoretically. Their work went on until 1756, and, as a result of such gradual study, they really gained extensive knowledge in physical chemistry. Among the papers in the archives quite a few notes have been preserved which deal with the experiments in physical chemistry; we are able to reconstruct their program in full, and even have some of their experimental results. But not one of the laboratory journals of this period (1752 to 1756) has yet been found in the archives, so we have no way of knowing what part of the proposed program was carried out.

Lomonosov's physicochemical experiments were conceived on very broad principles according to a program so all-embracing that it has not even yet been exhausted. Its chief attention was focused on what we now call solutions, which are formed by water and other liquids with salts and other substances. Before working out the properties of solvents experimentally, he wrote an interesting article about the action of chemical solvents in general (1745) in which he examines the mechanism of solution itself. While this has no interest today, the important fact is that Lomonosov made a strict distinction between two cases of solubility and examined each separately with care: (a) solution accompanied by the liberation of heat, for instance metal in acid, that is, in essence a chemical mutual reaction (because, from the solution received, when it is evaporated there is obtained not the original metal but that salt of it which was formed by the given acid); (b) solution accompanied by the absorption of heat, for instance, salt in water, in which no chemical change in the dissolved substance results but, when the solution is evaporated, the same salt crystallizes as was originally dissolved. Later, in 1789, Lavoisier made such a distinction between the kinds of solution.

Further, the program of experiments provided for the study of the products of the crystallization of solutions—the crystals of different salts. For these it was necessary to investigate their solubility in water under different temperatures, specific gravity, hardness, and several other properties; in all, these programs cover several pages. Notes of the results which have been preserved show that Lomonosov devoted his chief attention to determining the solubility of salts under different temperatures, from 0° to 150° on Lomonosov's thermometer (Chapter 3) that is, from 0° to 100°C. These experiments usually gave lower results than contemporary ones do. Later, in 1819, Gay-Lussac made similar experiments, as did many other scholars after him. Lomonosov had to overcome tremendous difficulties in physicochemical experiments; the technique for the determinations had not been evolved at all; he had to invent not only the apparatus but also the methods of investigation. The apparatus was produced with extreme slowness and the methods of investigation gave divergent results. In consequence, we have here, as in the other provinces of Lomonosov's scientific work, valuable ideas and brilliant visions of those paths by which the development of science was to proceed: but of practical results from these ideas and foresights there were none because of the complete lack of indispensable apparatus as well as of methods of investigation. The ideas anticipate their practical realization by a century and a half.

In the preceding pages we became acquainted with Lomonosov as a university teacher. His method of teaching was quite contemporary: first he read lectures in chemistry, accompanying them with experiments and examinations; later he gave the students a broad practical course in laboratory work, in which their understanding of the theoretical propositions of the lecture was reinforced by independent work. The students' mastery of the course and skill in practical work were verified, then as now, by their ability to make independent investigations—research such as is now presented for a diploma. Some such work done by Klementyev has come down to us and reveals that he was fully acquainted with chemistry. As a teacher, Lomonosov was at the height of his professorial calling. So far as we know, his chemical laboratory was the first research and teaching laboratory anywhere. The second laboratory of this type, as we learn from the history of chemistry, was not founded until the nineteenth century by Professor Liebig in Giessen, Germany, where it opened in 1825. There the study and research work of the students, together with the scientific research of the professor himself and his assistants, were carried on as they had been in Lomonosov's laboratory.

During the nineteenth century chemists were often physicists as physicists also were chemists, so that all made use of the processes of both sciences in their work. Certain points of Lomonosov's comprehensive program of physico-chemical experiments were subjected to development and improvement, but there was no separate science of physical chemistry devoted to the elaboration of chemistry with the aid of physical methods. Such a science appeared only in the 1880's, when one of the first and most important pioneers in this direction was Wilhelm Ostwald, also of Russian descent. He delivered the first course in physical chemistry in the University of Leipzig about 1885, and he too built in the university a great physicochemical labora-tory, where in substance Lomonosov's program of experi-ments with solutions, of which Ostwald naturally knew nothing, was worked out. I informed him of this program in 1905.

The development of physical chemistry for the past fifty years has exceeded all expectations; in its turn, the develop-ment has had a highly beneficial effect on chemistry in general, introducing new quantitative methods and making exact much that had hitherto been unclear and contra-dictory. Physical chemistry more and more makes use of higher mathematics, which is absolutely indispensable for its further development. That triple alliance which Lomo-nosov once proclaimed of chemistry, physics, and mathe-matics became an accomplished fact. Just as weight, meas-ure, and number were introduced into chemistry with the help of physics, thereby converting it into an exact science, so today chemistry has begun to penetrate further and further into physics, thus creating a chemical physics. Either science is inconceivable without the other, and neither is possible without mathematics. As Lomonosov saw clearly, each supplements the other and leads to joint conquests in the realm of the unknown. He was the first physical chemist, the father of physical chemistry.

But this is not the whole story. As we recognize, Lomonosov on all occasions advanced another basic idea which was the cornerstone of his corpuscular philosophy: that the minute particles—corpuscules, atoms—determine the properties, or the physical and chemical nature, of all substances. He developed all this in the *Oration on the Use of Chemistry*, when referring primarily to physical chemistry: "Chemistry will be the prime leader in the discovery of the inner secret places of substances, will first permit acquaintance with the particles." Already in the *Elements of Mathematical Chemistry* he tries to sketch in outline the application of the atomic theory to chemistry. Throughout his life he meditated on this subject, and in the *Treatise on the Solid and Liquid States of Substances* he first speaks about the structure (his expression) of the particles or molecules: "Physicists, and especially chemists, will have to operate in darkness unless they learn the inner imperceptible structure of particles."

This prophecy of Lomonosov also was realized gradually, as the history of chemistry shows, during the course of the nineteenth century. Little by little chemistry turned into the science of molecules, which are constructed of atoms. After 1865 this extended to organic chemistry as well, and later to "complex compounds"—and toward the beginning of the twentieth century the existence of the atom and the molecule was proved by experiment. The structure, that is to say, the disposition of the atoms in the molecules, is known in almost all chemical elements and compounds except the very complex ones. Chemists are beginning to emerge from the darkness into the light. The further stages of development are known to all: the definition of the structure of the atom, the study of the influence of this structure on the chemical and other properties of the atom; the revelation of the structure of the molecule—not just of the mere disposition of atoms in it, but the nature of their interconnection. At the present time hundreds and thousands of scholars are straining their energies to realize Lomonosov's testament: "To investigate the elementary particles is as necessary as it is for the particles themselves to exist. And just as substances could not be formed without the imperceptible particles, so, without exploring these, the study of the most advanced physics is impossible."

We have come to the end of Lomonosov's activity as a chemist and physical chemist. As early as 1754, when making an award for a dissertation submitted for a prize in chemistry he declared that the author of it, if he should come to Russia, might become professor of chemistry since he himself, overburdened by other matters, could no longer be active in the field. U. Salkhov was invited to be his successor at the close of 1755. When Lomonosov moved from the Vasilyevsky Ostrov to his own house on the Moika, his work in the chemical laboratory ceased and was transferred to the laboratory he built in his own house. The chemical laboratory, on the construction of which he had expended so much strength and energy, existed until 1787 when, as was said in Chapter 3, a building for the Russian Academy (of Literature) was erected on the site of the botanical garden of the academy.

CHAPTER 6

Lomonosov, a member of the chancellery of the academy —The administration of the gymnasium and the university and their status—Project of statutes for them— Geographic department and maps of Russia—Economic maps—Discussion on greater accuracy of ocean navigation—Chemical and optical notes—Description of voyages in the northern seas and the expedition of Chichagov —Icebergs—The transit of Venus—Mutual relations between science and the church—The foundations of metallurgy—Catherine II and Lomonosov—On the strata of the earth and the occurrence of metals—Works in geology and mineralogy.

LOMONOSOV spent the last years of his life in the same feverish activity which occupied those that preceded. I shall begin this account with his work in the administration of the academy. As we have seen, in 1757 he was made a councillor of the chancellery. This consumed a great deal of time and had many disagreeable consequences both to himself and to the persons with whom he came into conflict. His new duties were performed just as conscientiously as his former ones. He tried to investigate everything and, by the force of his personality, constantly broadened the scope of affairs which, in his opinion, properly came under the jurisdiction of the chancellery. This gave rise to constant conflict with many of the academicians.

In March 1758, after Lomonosov had submitted to the president his views regarding the "superfluities, lacks, and confusions" which he discovered in the academy, the president entrusted him with special supervision of the historical and geographical collections of the academy, as well as of the university and gymnasium. From that time on Lomonosov exercised a great influence on academic affairs and did all he could to "bring the academy into a good condition." In 1761 he submitted a special note on this subject in which, along with a series of purely practical measures (for instance, that money assigned to the sciences be spent for no other purpose; that skilled workmen in the academy shops be required to work only for the members and not to seek work outside, and the like), he points out the necessity of removing Academicians Miller and Taubert, the "worthy" successor of Schumacher, who died in 1761. His repeated representations on this subject, especially in 1761 and 1762, however, had no results.

Lomonosov managed the gymnasium and the university connected with the Academy of Sciences until his death. He built a dormitory for the students, and did everything he could to make certain that the money apportioned for the maintenance of the gymnasium students would be paid on time (each received thirty-six rubles a year); he took care that the number of students should always equal the quota of forty; and, in 1759, he established rules for them, some excerpts of which are interesting. It was recommended "to apply the utmost diligence to the sciences and not to heed any other inclination"; to get along politely with the teachers, not to quarrel, not to prevent others from studying, not to use "words base and vulgar" in conversation. "When someone is reciting a lesson in response to a question of the teacher and does not know it thoroughly, the comrade sitting near him should not whisper advice to him and thus encourage his sloth. An abettor of this kind is subject to just the same punishment as the one who does not know." Cleanliness should be observed "not only in irreproachable work but also at table, and in caring for books, bed, and clothes." Sloth is of all things most harmful to students "and on that account should be overcome in every

way by obedience, temperance, watchfulness, and patience."
It was necessary to guard against "low, bad company, which
might soon lead to a do-nothing and idle life as well as
truancy from school."

Regardless of these excellent rules, the students undoubtedly led a hard life, and we frequently find descriptions of flights from the institution by students in which
even teachers took part. Thus, having fled in December
1762, the student Morozov and the teacher Golovin were
in hiding for more than a month with counterfeit passports.
Before escaping, Morozov stole the uniform cloak of another
student, Kosov. For these misdemeanors Morozov was
forced to serve in the army in 1763. In general, thefts also
were frequent among the students even though severe punishment was prescribed for this; thus it was ordered that
the student Arsenyev, convicted of drunkenness and thievery,
should be expelled and "have severe punishment by rods
inflicted on him in front of all the students and gymnasts,
and should be sent, with an explanatory note, to the War
Collegium [Ministry] to be conscripted as a soldier."

The gymnasium was located at that time in a rented
building which had fallen into complete disrepair. In the
winter the dough froze in the kneading trough in the kitchen
and the ink froze in the rooms. Broken panes in class-
room windows were patched with paper. The manner in
which lessons proceeded is described thus in the report of
the inspector: "The teachers in winter give lectures while
dressed in fur coats, moving back and forth in the class-
room, but the students, not equipped with warm clothes
and not having the freedom to rise from their places, shiver,
whereby arises an obstruction all through the body and then
mange and scurvy set in; because of these illnesses they are
obliged to give up attendance at classes. Thus it is not remarkable if the progress of the students is not in proportion
to the effort of the teachers."

Lomonosov had long wished to transfer the educational institutions to other premises, but a suitable occasion did not present itself until the autumn of 1764, when the house of Stroganov on the Malaya Neva was bought by the academy. Taubert, it is certain, had his eye on this building and intended to establish there an anatomist, an astronomer, and so on. Lomonosov had to carry on a long series of very sharp disputes with Taubert, but finally, with the help of the president, he was able to install in the house the university and gymnasium.

Commissioned by the president, Lomonosov drew up new regulations for the university, that is, a statutory project. He thought it necessary to reserve a series of special privileges to the university; namely, the right to award learned degrees, to give the students appropriate rank, to do away with the burdensome police surveillance, to grant vacations on holidays, and to allot sums of money in the first instance. All of these measures, so necessary to the successful administration of an institution of higher learning, were adopted only many years after Lomonosov's time. As early as the beginning of 1760 the president, noticing that Lomonosov through his efforts had brought the gymnasium into much better condition than before, handed over to him the establishment and administration of the university. He confirmed the rules of the university, whereby it consisted of three faculties—law, medicine, and philosophy; and the yearly grant for the needs of the university, together with the gymnasium, came to 15,248 rubles. But the privileges, which required the confirmation of the empress, were not realized.

The care with which Lomonosov managed the university and the gymnasium may be seen from the following incident with the inspector of the university commons, who since 1755 had been K. Moderach. In 1761 the students submitted a complaint about him, calling attention to the monotony of the institution's food. Moderach himself presented a petition for his own retirement. Lomonosov accepted it and appointed S. Kotelnikov inspector, "who, as a native Russian, would take better care of the students than of his own relatives." However, the matter was delayed because of the president's absence, and the students presented a new complaint against Moderach. The matter ended when Lomonosov dismissed him on his own authority and took most decisive measures to have him removed from his official quarters. When the president heard of this he suggested to Moderach that he lodge a complaint against Lomonosov in court if he thought he had been wronged, but that there were no obstacles to his retirement if he himself wished it. Moderach chose the latter course and received an official discharge. From the report Lomonosov presented in 1763 it is apparent that during the period of his management of the gymnasium twenty persons finished the course, whereas during the time of his predecessor, Schumacher, there was not one who completed it. Moreover, Lomonosov requested that the sum alloted to each student be increased to forty-eight rubles a year, which required "only 720 rubles, the only sum in the academy which is not spent on parasites."

The department of geography, of which Lomonosov became the head in 1757, was founded at the Academy of Sciences "for the study of matters which pertain to Russian geography," and its chief task was the preparation of accurate maps of Russia, constantly checking and revising them by means of new information coming into the department. The department consisted of professors and instructors with students working under their direction. In 1745 this department brought out an atlas of Russia, the maps of which later proved to be inaccurate in many respects. For twelve years previous to 1757 nothing had been done to correct them, and when Lomonosov entered upon his duties he decided first of all to undertake the preparation of maps as nearly exact as possible. To this end a questionnaire of thirty points was drawn up. These points were carefully examined in sessions of the conference, and later, toward the end of 1759 and 1760, the questionnaire was sent through the senate to all towns for an early reply. The questions related to "the size of the cities, the number of stone and wooden houses, on what river or lake they stand, when the fairs take place, what sort of businesses and crafts there are, what sort of workshops, factories, mills, arable land, and forests; on which hand, looking downstream the hilly [bluff] side of the river lies, where the landing places are, when the rivers open up and when they freeze over; at what distance the neighboring towns are situated; where there are notable and high mountains; what kinds of grain are sown more than others and which ones yield best," and a series of other economic problems. If there are any plans or records in the town, copies of them should be sent. The *Kammerkollegia*[1] was asked to furnish the number of souls in each village so that the large ones should not be omitted and the small recorded and the proportion thus be lost. Information on the monasteries and churches was requested of the holy synod. Appropriations for travel and subsidiary expenses were obtained from the senate for two geographical expeditions to "determine the longitude and latitude of important places by means of astronomical observations." These expeditions, however, were not equipped in spite of all Lomonosov's attempts. During his life, likewise, the replies to the questionnaire that were received were not put to use, and the undertaking, which he had set up on such a large scale, thus failed to yield results—certainly, not without the help of his enemies.

In this enterprise of Lomonosov we see one of the meth-

[1] Government department with functions of a finance ministry. ED.

ods of collective work which now give the most valuable
results; the gifted leader distributes the work among a great
number of collaborators, to each of whom small definite
tasks are given. Then the joint results enable them to proceed to conclusions of the highest importance. In the case
described the numerous local correspondents, fulfilling their
tasks precisely, would have allowed Lomonosov to make a
complete picture of the economic geography of the Russia
of those times. The answers of these correspondents were
preserved and may be seen even today. Lomonosov proposed
that they be utilized to found a government department of
rural economy so that, through a network of on-the-spot
correspondents, information about sowing, harvesting, and
other economic matters could be collected.

A serious illness which lasted almost all of 1762 made it
impossible for Lomonosov to be frequently in the academy;
he discussed chancellery matters at his home and signed
papers there. In the beginning of 1763, when he was in
condition to drive to the academy, Taubert showed him a
presidential order of August 31, 1762, to transfer the management of the department of geography to Academician
G. Miller. Embittered and offended, Lomonosov wrote at
once to the president an account of all that had been done
under his direction in the department and refused to obey
the order, which had already been held up for more than
half a year, "clear witness to the fact that it had been requested by schemers for private ends."

Such a transfer of the management of the department of
geography to G. Miller was probably connected with the
order given him and Taubert to make maps of the agricul-
tural products and wares produced in different parts of
Russia. When Lomonosov found out about it, he boldly
wrote his observations on this order, proving its impractica-
bility in the form in which it was proposed, and submitted
to the senate a declaration that such an undertaking would

hinder him from finishing his atlas of Russia. Thereafter, Lomonosov was entrusted with the compilation of "economic landmaps," but his death soon thereafter prevented him from carrying out this enterprise.

Quite naturally, as the head of the department of geography, Lomonosov became occupied with geography generally and the sciences closely connected with it. Therefore, we have a whole series of important works dating from the last years of his life which relate to these subjects. Of first importance was the learned speech delivered on May 8,

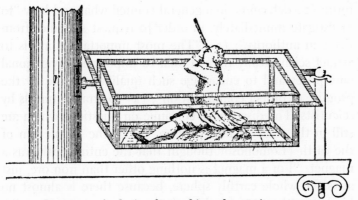

Lomonosov's device for making observations at sea.

1759, *A Dissertation on Greater Exactitude in Navigation.* It is divided into three parts: the first treats of the determination of latitude and longitude in clear weather; the second, finding latitude and longitude in cloudy weather; while the third discusses scientific ocean navigation.

All three parts abound in original ideas and propositions which reveal Lomonosov's inventiveness and originality. The questions he examines are among those which are still being investigated by specialists in physical geography. In the first two parts many new kinds of apparatus are described, some of which were later proposed by others; but these devices were insufficiently elaborated, and since they were not actually put into practice, they failed to exert any influence on the history of the naval sciences.

Especially interesting is the third part, in which he developed a project for the founding of a grandiose international institution, the Academy of Navigation. In this academy trained mathematicians, astronomers, hydrographers, and mechanicians "would strive only to increase the safety of seafaring by means of new and useful inventions"; for this they would (1) select from all books everything that was useful for navigation and issue it in a condensed form; (2) determine in a general council what and how "to investigate immediately, in order to request subsidies from those in authority"; (3) "The most important thing is to attract scientifically trained men to important navigational enterprises and to encourage such qualified people by the promise of proper compensation"; (4) to arrange travels by scientists. The discussions continue on questions which are still in the stage of investigation—about the magnetism of the earth (Lomonosov thought that the entire earth was a magnet: "For a magnet is nothing other than iron ore, just as is the whole earthly sphere, because there is almost no kind of earth, or stone, which does not show signs of iron."); about the force of gravity and its temporal changes; and finally about the possibility of forecasting the weather and those methods of barometric observation whereby he hoped to accomplish it. And to carry out these observations it was necessary to set up self-recording meteorological observatories in all parts of the earth.

Lomonosov was an active worker for the utmost perfection of marine instruments, telescopes, and other apparatus. The results of this activity for the years 1762 and 1763 have been preserved in the form of handwritten notes under the heading of *Chemical and Optical Notes*. This work has been studied in detail by Academician S. I. Vavilov, who has pointed out the far-reaching significance of the project for constructing a new telescope which is splendidly developed in these notes; similar ideas were expressed by others considerably later. In these same notes there also occurs a remarkable proposition on the determination of the relative strength of the light of the stars. Here Lomonosov first proposed a photometer, which was not introduced by others until the nineteenth century. It may be added that the ideas he advanced in these notes came into general scientific use only after a hundred years. In like manner he also worked a great deal during these years on the force of gravity. This subject interested him all through his life. He wrote about it to Euler in 1748 and later in several reports of the conference of the academy as well as in his own dissertations. Especially in the later years of his life, he studied the force of gravity. In order to observe it he constructed a great pendulum in his home, the oscillations of which "made the changes of the center of gravity of the earth unquestionable since these changes are periodic and are approximately in agreement with the phases of the moon. At any time of the year, in any condition of the atmosphere, in a warm or a cold room, they always show identical periods before and after noon." We know that tables of these observations were printed and also a dissertation about them written but neither has yet been found.

His occupation with matters concerning the sea probably aroused Lomonosov to work out and present, in September 1763, to the general-admiral, nine-year-old Grand Duke Pavel Petrovich,[2] "a short description of various travels in the northern seas and the indications of a possible passage to East India through the Siberian Ocean." This description is interesting for its appended map of the polar lands, which shows how little was known in those days about the northern shores of America and Asia. It also contains the develop-

[2] Who ascended the throne in 1796 as Tsar Paul I. ED.

ment of the idea Lomonosov had long entertained about
the northern route to India. As a matter of fact, as early as
1752, in the ode on Elizabeth's accession to the throne, he
speaks thus:

> In vain does Nature's frowning face
> Conceal from us the entrance place
> From evening's shores to land of morn;
> For lo, I see with clever eyes:
> Midst ice a Rus Columbus flies
> And laughs his destiny to scorn.

In an account of his occupations in 1755 Lomonosov
writes that he "has composed a letter on the northern route
to East India by the Siberian Ocean." He studied thoroughly
the accounts and the ships' logs of the expeditions which
had been ordered to the Arctic Ocean, and also collected
all available information from the Russian fishers and fur
traders who had been there. All this research was reflected
in the first song of the heroic poem, *Peter the Great* (1760).

The project of the northern passage was received at court
with full sympathy, and the young "general-admiral" sent
it to the Marine Commission of Russian Fleets with instructions that, if they did not find the project impossible, he be
advised so that he might report it to the empress. Traders
and coast dwellers were summoned by the commission, and
after the conferences with them Lomonosov drew up a new
detailed program for the expedition, which was fitted out
on May 14, 1764, under his direct supervision. Twenty
thousand rubles were appropriated for the expedition, rewards and ranks were promised to all participants, with
pensions to their widows in case of their death. Lomonosov
applied himself to this undertaking with all his ardor and
busied himself in equipping the ships with necessary supplies, instruments, and trained officers, but his death prevented him from carrying the project to conclusion.

However, he had prepared everything with such care that a few weeks following his death, on May 9, 1765, Admiral V. Chichagov, the leader of the expedition, left for Archangel with three ships. But not that year nor the next were their attempts to penetrate the solid ice crowned with success; after barely reaching eighty degrees north latitude, Chichagov was obliged to return to Archangel. His report says: "The impossibility of reaching the desired place has been revealed, whereof no doubt remains." In his project Lomonosov pointed out that the only clear path by which it was possible to reach the North Pole lay between the islands of Spitzbergen and Novaya Zemlya. Later, English and German scientists came to the same conclusion. The open Polar Sea up to seventy-nine degrees north latitude was discovered in September 1871 by the Austrian expedition on the *Tegetthoff*, under the command of Payer. Thus Lomonosov's assumptions were justified; after 108 years Payer, following Lomonosov's route, showed what profound knowledge of the Arctic Sea had inspired the Russian scholar when he drew up the project.

In the eighteenth century Lomonosov's project could not be realized as a result of both the insufficiency of technical means and the state of science. The project was at least 150 years ahead of its time. Only now, today, the construction in the north of dozens of meteorological stations, the radio, airplanes, icebreakers, and the force of steam have permitted the U.S.S.R. to make full use of Lomonosov's ideas and bring them to fruition.

Another interesting work of Lomonosov, *Ideas on the Origin of Icebergs in the Northern Seas*, also written in 1763, is, of course, a result of that same study of the conditions in the Arctic Sea which he pursued for his project of the expedition. He presented this report to the Swedish Academy of Sciences, which in that year had elected him an honorary member. Here he indicates, as the basis of his experiments, that in the open sea, in freezing cold, only a thin coating of ice can be formed from sea water; ice fields or ice masses caught on sand banks have their origin in the mouths of great rivers which flow into the Arctic Sea, whereas icebergs or floes owe their origin to the steep shores of the sea. All these are remarkable opinions for their time. It has now become clearly established that icebergs originate from glaciers which descend in Arctic countries directly to sea level. A glacier follows its course as long as it moves along the bottom of the sea. Then, when as a result of its continued forward movement the glacier begins to float in sufficiently deep water, pieces break off and become "icebergs." The iceberg forms a vertical wall which sinks deep into the sea and sometimes, as in the Antarctic countries, stretches for hundreds of kilometers.

The methods of determining latitude and longitude are directly connected with astronomical observations which Lomonosov also made. Of such observations made by him, those of May 26, 1761, deserve special mention. The astronomers of that time were awaiting this day with impatience, for a very rare astronomical phenomenon was to occur—the passage of the planet Venus over the sun's disc—an event which is not expected to occur again until 2004. As the English astronomer Halley had pointed out in 1691, from the time required for this passage it is possible to calculate exactly the distance of the earth from the sun. The academy sent two expeditions to Siberia, where this phenomenon was to occur later than in St. Petersburg (where it began at four o'clock in the morning). They returned empty-handed since, as the result of cloudy weather on that day, the sun was not visible. In St. Petersburg the day was preceded by some lively clashes among the academicians in which Lomonosov also took part. By a ukase of the senate, the responsibility for observations in the astronomical observatory was taken from Academician Epirus and handed over to the Russian scholars Krasilnikov and Kurganov.

The weather was excellent in St. Petersburg that morning, and the phenomenon could be observed in all its details. Lomonosov observed it at his own house and the results of his observations were later published in an article, *The Appearance of Venus on the Sun, Observed in the St. Petersburg Academy of Sciences on the 26th Day of May of the year 1761*. In this article the observations of Krasilnikov and Kurganov are described first, followed by his own. He was not so much interested in determining the exact moments when the disc of Venus entered and left the sun as in observing the phenomenon in general. And, as a matter of fact, it gave him the opportunity to make an interesting discovery. He noticed that, when the planet entered the solar disc, the edge of the disc became hazy, "whereas before that the edge had been even and clear all over; however, not having discerned any blackness, and thinking that a weary eye was the cause of the cloudiness, I left the telescope." When Venus approached the other side of the sun's edge to within a tenth part of its diameter, "there appeared on the edge of the sun a blister, which became more clearly defined the nearer Venus came to passing off. Soon this blister disappeared and Venus suddenly appeared without an edge. The complete exit, or the last contact of Venus' rear edge with the sun at the moment of exit, also took place with some tearing and with lack of clarity on the edge of the sun."

All of the astronomers who were then observing this passage saw these very same phenomena, and some of them mentioned it. But none of them drew the same conclusions as did Lomonosov: "According to these observations the Councillor Lomonosov reasons that the planet Venus is surrounded by a considerable atmosphere equal to, if not greater than, that which envelops our earthly sphere." Like almost all of his scientific discoveries, this too went unnoticed—and even now the discovery of the atmosphere of Venus is attributed to Schroeter and Herschel (1791).[3]

Lomonosov points out in a supplement to the article on the passage of Venus that it is possible to draw the conclusion, from the existence of an atmosphere around the planet, that it is a place of habitation for living beings. He declares himself in favor of teaching the multitude of worlds, and proves by texts from the "fathers of the Church," Basil the Great and John of Damascus, that this teaching does not contradict Holy Writ: "The Creator gave the human race two books: in the one he demonstrates his magnificence; in the other, his will. The first is this visible world, which he created in order that man, looking at the immensity, the beauty, and the symmetry of his structures, should admit the divine omnipotence in so far as understanding has been granted him. The second book is the sacred writ. In it is displayed the divine good will for our salvation. . . . In the book of the constitution of this visible world, physicists, mathematicians, astronomers, and other expounders of the divine actions which influence nature are the same as are the prophets, the apostles, and the teachers of the church in the second book. The mathematician is not sound in judgment if he wishes to measure the divine will with a compass; nor is the teacher of theology if he thinks that he is able to study astronomy or chemistry from the psalter."

These words, bold for that time, show how Lomonosov regarded the interrelation of science and religion; they are

[3] According to Gerard P. Kuiper of the Yerkes Observatory, what Lomonosov here observed "is the so-called 'black drop,' a well-known phenomenon in Venus transits on which there is an extensive literature. This 'black drop' has nothing to do with the presence or absence of a Venus atmosphere and can in no case be regarded as a proof of its existence. Mercury, which does not have an atmosphere, shows a 'black drop' also. It is caused by diffraction and physiological effects of the observer." ED.

an answer to the holy synod's proposal to the empress (1757) to issue a ukase, unquestionably directed against Lomonosov, "in order that none henceforth shall dare to write or print anything either of the multitude of worlds, or of anything else in opposition to the sacred faith, or in disagreement with honorable morals, under the penalty of most severe punishment."

Of course I need hardly add that according to the most recent studies the atmosphere of the planet Venus, which is undoubtedly very great, consists mainly of carbonic gas and therefore living beings would not survive.

In a second supplement, Lomonosov speaks of the teaching of Copernicus concerning the movement of the earth around the sun and includes a short poem (the theme is borrowed from the works of Cyrano de Bergerac, a French writer of the seventeenth century) about a clever cook who declared himself in favor of Copernicus' system, on the suggestion of his master:

> Once, feasting, two astronomers were seated,
> And argued 'mongst themselves in language heated.
> Earth turning travels round the Sun, did one
>   maintain,
> The other that Sun leads the planets in its train.
> This one was Ptolemy, the first, Copernicus.
> The smiling Cook resolved their quarrel thus:
> Knowst thou the course of stars? the host inquired,
> Then how to solve this question art inspired?
> Copernicus was right, the answer went.
> I'll prove it true, although I've never spent
> Time on the Sun. What Cook of brains could boast
> So few, to turn the Hearth about the Roast?

Lomonosov's interest in astronomy and his acquaintance with this science is proved in a work of his recently unearthed in the archives of the Academy of Sciences, A *New*

Method, Very Exact and Simple, to Find and Describe the Meridian Line. Professor A. A. Ivanov, who at my request has examined this work, considers that it presents a method which was new and highly original for its time.

One circumstance in Lomonosov's scientific activity is very interesting. He was sent abroad for the special task of studying mining and metallurgy, but, although he undoubtedly became thoroughly acquainted with these applied sciences, never in all his life did he apply them practically. We do not know what considerations were the cause of this, but the fact itself is unquestionable. Soon after his return to St. Petersburg, as he himself says in 1742, he wrote the book, *The First Principles of the Science of Mining,* and the manuscript of the first part of it has been found among his papers. Later he worked it over into *The First Principles of Metallurgy, or of the Treatment of Ores,* but did not have it printed until twenty years later, at the end of 1761. It actually came out in November 1763 without any change in the original text. It is not known why Lomonosov failed to include in it the discoveries of new metals—for instance, platinum, cobalt, and nickel—which were made during this period, the improvements in the methods of extracting metals, or the observations which he had himself made.

Lomonosov's *Metallurgy* contains a long dedication to Catherine II which has historical interest. At the end of 1761 Elizabeth Petrovna, who was in general favorably disposed toward Lomonosov, died and Peter III succeeded to the throne. He did not reign for long, since on June 28, 1762, as the result of a palace revolution, his wife, Catherine Alekseyevna, ascended the throne and on July 6 Peter himself was killed. Catherine II had known Lomonosov for a long time. There is evidence that he presented her with a collection of his works in 1751, and sometimes traveled to see her in Oranienbaum. But on her accession to the throne (which Lomonosov celebrated in an ode) not one of the rewards which she issued with a lavish hand was conferred on Lomonosov, and he, at the end of July 1762, submitted a petition for his discharge with a pension. No result was forthcoming, and not until April 23, 1763, did Catherine write to Olsufyev: "Adam Vasilyevich, I believe Lomonosov is poor; confer with the hetman as to whether it is not possible to give him a pension, and give me an answer." (The hetman was the president of the academy, Count Razumovsky.) After a few days the senate received a ukase: "We have awarded Collegiate Councillor Mikhail Lomonosov the rank of state councillor and permanent retirement from service with half pay until his death. Catherine, Moscow, the second day of May, 1763."

Lomonosov learned about this rather quickly in St. Petersburg, on May 15. But he could not know that two days previously Catherine had sent a note to the senate, which was then located in Moscow: "If the ukase about the retirement of Lomonosov has not yet been sent from the senate to St. Petersburg, then it shall be returned to me." This was done, so that our academician continued in all his capacities. In August of that same year, on the authority of the senate, the Academy of Sciences drew up plans for a monument in memory of Catherine II's accession to the throne, with mosaic pictures by Lomonosov. The dedication of the *Metallurgy* to Catherine was dated October 11, 1763, and the presentation of the book to her probably took place at the end of November. In this dedication the full importance of metallurgy for the state was examined in detail. After this, Catherine became more favorably inclined toward Lomonosov. By her special ukase of December 20 of that year he was made a state councillor with an increase of salary to 1,875 rubles a year.

Metallurgy, the art of extracting metals from ores, was described by Lomonosov according to the material which he collected during his stay abroad; that is, the method of the German metallurgists of the second quarter of the eighteenth century. In addition to the processes of extraction, the properties of the metals under observation and the means of determining the degree of their purity and the admixtures in them are described as well as chemical operations which lead to that goal—that is, a guide to the art of assaying is given. This part of the work has only an historical interest today and, as already has been noted, was out of date even when the book appeared. On the other hand, the supplement to the *Metallurgy*, which is almost as large as the book itself, is profoundly interesting. It is called *On the Strata of the Earth* and should be considered along with the *Speech on the Birth of Metals from the Shaking of the Earth, delivered on the Sixth Day of September of the Year 1757.* Here we have Lomonosov's views on geological phenomena, on the origin of ore and metallic rocks, and the like—pioneering views in his time.

In the middle of the eighteenth century, mineralogy and geology were perhaps on an even lower level than chemistry. There were at that time two schools of thought in the field of mineralogy: the followers of the first scrutinized all phenomena from the point of view of philosophy—that is, they strove to conceive, clearly and exactly, the tasks and goals of mineralogical science in general in their relation to a broad *Weltanschauung* which embraced all nature. Lomonosov belonged to this group. Those representing the other school were pure practicians who collected material and set it in a framework established by custom or by preconceived views. These were the naturalist-empiricists.

Soon after Lomonosov's death Gailloui and Werner, two scholars who first became active in the 1770's, appeared. Both were naturalist-empiricists, and the quality and significance of their achievements was such that the work of their predecessors was soon pushed into the background and forgotten. This lot befell Lomonosov's work since the academician mineralogists closest to him were warm advocates of Werner and Gailloui. Nevertheless, in his general views and hypothesis in this field, Lomonosov was far in advance of his contemporaries. For example, consider the fundamental idea which pervaded everything he wrote on geology, an idea indisputably correct but utterly new and revolutionary for his time—namely, the idea on the constant evolution which goes on in nature. This is expressed in paragraph 98 of the *Strata of the Earth*: "It is necessary constantly to remember that the visible corporeal objects on earth and the entire world were not in the beginning created in precisely the same form that we now find them, but they have undergone great changes, as history and ancient geography, compared to present geographic science, show, and as the changes in the surface of the earth which are taking place in our time also reveal. . . . And thus many vainly think that everything we see was so made by the Creator from the beginning, that not only mountains, valleys, and waters but also various kinds of minerals came into being with the rest of the world, and therefore it is not necessary to investigate the causes for their differing in their internal properties and distribution. Such opinions are extremely harmful to the development of all the sciences, and consequently to the growth of knowledge of the nature of this earthly sphere, especially as it affects the art of mining. It is very easy for these know-it-alls to be philosophers and repeat the three words which they have learned by heart, 'God thus created,' in answer to every question instead of discussing the causes involved."

To my way of thinking, the most important opinion was the one first expressed by Lomonosov regarding the formation of veins in ore deposits and the determination of their age. In this he was earlier than Werner. According to his opinion, veins of ore are formed in clefts of rocks into which penetrate aqueous solutions of the different substances deposited in these crevices. The veins are of different age since some of them intersect others, and in such cases veins of different ages carry different minerals. Veins destroyed by earthquakes form pockets of ore, and veins that have been completely shattered yield granules so that the material found in the veins is mixed up with pulverized layers of rock. The formation of veins is discussed in detail in the *Discourse on the Origin of Metals*. In describing different types of earthquakes, Lomonosov was the first to speak of the wavelike vibrations of the surface of the earth, sixty years before Jong, to whom the discovery is usually ascribed. He was the first to express a conception of imperceptible earthquakes, that is, those which, in contrast with palpable earthquakes, are not noticed although, because of their frequently prolonged duration, they produce considerable effect. Such quakes became the subject of study only in the second half of the nineteenth century.

Earthquakes produce clefts in rock which later fill up with aqueous solutions of various substances and thus give rise to veins of ore. In the clefts also appear volcanic mountains, volcanoes, from which the substances forming the lower strata of the earth issue under the pressure of the upper layers. All these are views which became widespread only at the end of the nineteenth century.

All mountains and other features of the earth's relief Lomonosov explains by the settling and other movements of the earth's crust and by the erosion of the surface by rain water, and he sees the cause of these movements in the internal fire arising from the spontaneous combustion of sulphur and similar materials under the influence of tremendous pressure and friction of the layers, that is, from chemical energy. He attempted to define the depth at which this occurs, on the basis of various assumptions, and came to the conclusion that it is vast and that the hard crust of the earth possesses great thickness. Finally, he pointed out the dependence of an earthquake's form on the depth below the earth's surface of the internal fire. All these opinions later reappeared in the nineteenth century.

In the field of geology Lomonosov's opinions were likewise much in advance of his time. He was the first to present in scientific form the question of the age of mountains and evinced a very critical attitude of doubt concerning the catastrophes to which was then attributed the destruction of organisms that have been metamorphosed into fossils. He believed that the organisms met their end by the same causes that operate today—through flood, earthquakes, and so on—and that their age was determined by the sequence of the strata in which they were found. Lomonosov credited the organic world with an enormous significance in the life of our planet: thus, from the products of the destruction of plant remains peat is formed, a substance Lomonosov unquestionably knew existed, although it was still unknown in Russia. Other similar products are lignite and coal and the petroleum and other mineral fuels obtained from them by dry distillation. Finally, the rotting of vegetable remains produces the humus of the soil, which he called "chernozem" (black earth). (This is not the same "black earth" which is now found in our southeastern regions—Lomonosov was not acquainted with that soil.) None of these ideas became current until the nineteenth century. It is especially interesting that Lomonosov also took chemical theories into consideration in connection with all of his other theories.

In conclusion, Lomonosov everywhere stresses the necessity of inculcating exact methods and a thorough understanding of chemistry, physics, and mathematics in geology: "Here are the bowels of the earth, here are the strata, here are the veins of other materials which Nature has produced in the depths. Let man notice their distribution, color, weight; let him use, in his reflections, the counsel of mathematics, of chemistry, and of physics in general" (Paragraph 96).

In explaining chemical phenomena he makes use of the theory of phlogiston, probably in order to be more comprehensible to his hearers and readers, who were undoubtedly acquainted with the basic chemical hypothesis of the time. In general, Lomonosov was the first to present a survey of the mineral kingdom in the Russian language, and his *First Principles* remained the foremost original Russian work with a description of minerals until the end of the eighteenth century. Only in 1796 and 1798 did the mineralogies of Teryaev and Severgin appear, written in the spirit of Werner and Gailloui.

Lomonosov was also interested in minerals in the last years of his life. He was the first to describe the red Siberian lead ore, later called "krokoit." It was not until 1766 that Academician Leman gave a description of it. And then in December 1763 he undertook a huge task, *A General System of Russian Mineralogy*, which he planned to organize collectively with the help of correspondents scattered throughout Russia. To this undertaking he wished to attract not only manufacturers and proprietors of ore deposits but other persons also. In this venture Lomonosov appears in the role of a modern regional specialist collecting information on natural phenomena.

CHAPTER 7

*On the increase and preservation of the Russian people—
Work in Russian history—Voltaire's history of Peter the
Great—Making copies of frescoes—A. L. Schlözer—
Lomonosov's work in the development of the Russian
language; the creation of a literary language—Lomono-
sov's three styles—Russian grammar—Scientific language
—Lomonosov's poetry—Natural science in his verses—
Festival odes and their influence—Illuminations—Lomo-
nosov's relations with other writers: Sumarokov, Tredya-
kovsky.*

I N THE preceding chapters I spoke of the different
aspects of Lomonosov's amazingly versatile scientific
work and confined myself to a mere mention of his
literary, philological, and other works. In order to give
a rounded picture of his genius, we must, before we can
complete this biography of Lomonosov, describe those aspects of his seething activity which have not yet been referred to in this short treatment. Let us first examine his
remarkable letter to I. I. Shuvalov of November 1, 1761,
On the Increase and Preservation of the Russian People,
which first came to light in its entirety in 1871. Here we see
a new Lomonosov, the statesman, analyzing from a political
point of view the question of the importance of increasing
the population and pointing out keenly and sagaciously the
defects of the society of his time.

Lomonosov divides the policy necessary to increase population into measures to increase the birthrate, to preserve
the newborn children, and to provide for the admission of
foreigners to Russian citizenship. For the most productive
"maternal fecundity" it is necessary: (1) to eliminate marriages between persons of unsuitable ages; (2) to abolish

compulsory marriages; (3) to abolish the law forbidding marriage more than three times; (4) to forbid young widowed priests and deacons to become monks, and forbid laymen to become monks until the age of forty-five to fifty.

To preserve those children that are born it is necessary: (5) to found poorhouses for the care of illegitimate children; (6) to fight infant diseases; (7) always to baptize children in warm water ("The priests follow the instruction of the Service Book[1] that the water should be natural and without contamination, and consider heat to be an admixed substance. But they do not realize that in the summer they baptize with warm water, which according to this reasoning is polluted, thus contradicting themselves, and through their own stupidity do not know that there is much heat even in very cold water. . . . However, there is no need to discuss physics with uneducated priests; it is sufficient to compel them by authority always to baptize with warm water heated to the equivalence of summer temperature"); (8) to strive against intemperance; (9) to organize necessary medical aid against sickness; (10) to take all possible measures against the plague, fires, floods, freezing, etc.; (11) to take measures to prevent murder in quarrels and in robberies; (12) to prevent migration and flight from the central provinces to the border.

This is all set forth in lively picturesque language. Here follows a description of the excesses then common at the end of the fasts: "The bright Easter of Christ is approaching, the universal joy of Christians. Although folk read unceasingly and repeat constantly the passion of the Lord, still our thoughts are already on Easter Week. One anticipates pleasant food; another wonders whether his new clothes will be ready for the holiday; another pictures how merry he will be with his relatives and friends; another prepares colored eggs and undoubtedly finds opportunity to

[1] *Trebnik* (Book of Needs). ED.

kiss the pretty girls or to arrange a better rendezvous. Finally they begin matins at midnight and finish singing the Eucharist at dawn. 'Christ is risen' is only in their ears and on their tongues, but what room is there for it in their hearts where all the smallest crevices are filled with worldly desires? Like dogs let off the leash, like stored-up water from behind a bursting dam, like whirlwinds breaking out from a cloud, they explode, they smash, they rush, they overthrow, they tear to pieces; here fragments of different meats and broken dishes are scattered about, drinks are spilled and lie in puddles—there men lie, unconscious, overpowered with gluttony and drunkenness, there they loll about unmasked, the very folk who were recently fasting strictly."

In Lomonosov's view the fasts would be less harmful at another time of the year and, in general, he declared against the habit of fasting as having "nothing in common with penance." He saw in the fasts one of the chief causes of the death rate of the people. This note of Lomonosov's probably contributed its share of benefit; but it did not receive sufficient publicity, for the thoughts expressed were too revolutionary for the time.

He wanted to write a few more notes on similar themes, and collected his ideas for the following letters: (a) on rooting out idleness; (b) on improving morals and on the greater enlightenment of the people; (c) on the reform of agriculture; (d) on the improvement and increase of trades and arts; (e) on better profits for the merchant class; (f) on better national economy; (g) on preserving the art of war during a period of prolonged peace. Whether these were actually written is not known; we do not possess them at the present time.

Lomonosov's labors in Russian history are connected with these essays. He had long since begun to occupy himself with this subject. In 1749, when the academicians were examining the speech which had been prepared for the public meeting of the academy by Academician G. F. Miller on *The Origin of the People and the Name of Russia*, he spoke long and heatedly on the beginnings of Rus and on the coming of the Varangians. Lomonosov thought they were Slavonic in origin, while Miller attributed Swedish ancestry to them. The proofs which Lomonosov advanced show that even then he had read a great deal on the subject and had formed definite opinions. The long scientific controversies which took place on this occasion probably contributed no little to the rise and intensification of the hostile relations which later existed between Lomonosov and G. F. Miller.

From 1751 he worked at history more seriously and with increasing interest, for at that time Empress Elizabeth expressed a desire to see a history of Russia written by Lomonosov's pen. He prepared with great zeal to carry out her wish and made himself acquainted with a long list of sources. His first historical work, *A Short Russian Chronicle, with Genealogy*, appeared in 1760. It contains a synopsis of the most important acts of the grand princes and tsars to the time of Peter I inclusively. The first part of the history was entirely ready for the press before Lomonosov's death and was printed after his death, in 1766, by the Academy of Sciences under the title of *Ancient Russian History From the Beginnings of the Russian People Until the Death of the Grand Prince Yaroslav the First, or until 1054.*

This history may be divided into two parts. The first, dealing with the origin of the Russian people, is of special interest. Lomonosov, a scholar who saw in all things the idea of evolution, applied this concept to history. In the *History* he takes into consideration the frequent intermixing of peoples as a result of war and continual migrations. Generally speaking, in the opinion of specialists his opinions retain, even now, their value. On the other hand, the second section, which treats historical periods, presents nothing original and is essentially a literary version of the chronicles, retelling them in new language.

In 1757 and the years following, Lomonosov, in the capacity of historian, took part in a curious affair. Elizabeth had commissioned Voltaire to write a history of Peter I, and Shuvalov asked Lomonosov to collect and deliver the necessary materials. So far as we can judge by Lomonosov's letters, he made a considerable number of summaries and extracts which were later translated into French and sent off to Voltaire. The further history of this affair, according to the story of Academician Stählin, was that, in addition to material for the history, they sent presents of great value to the famous author from time to time in order to inspire him to treat with proper seriousness the commission which had been given to him. But what a surprise for the court when the history finally appeared! It was a bare skeleton. Voltaire did not use half of the information which had been sent him, but merely kept it for himself. On the other hand he substituted many of his own quite incorrect fabrications. Mainly for patriotic reasons, in 1761 Lomonosov wrote his own observations on this book, drawing attention to a series of errors incorporated by Voltaire.

Since he set great store by Russian antiquity, Lomonosov proposed sending an artist to make copies of the frescoes and pictures of past rulers in ancient churches. Means for this purpose had been provided, all necessary licenses from the synod were obtained, and an artist, A. Grekov, had been found, but on Taubert's recommendation Grekov was appointed tutor to Grand Duke Paul Petrovich and had to remain in Petersburg. Thus Lomonosov's plans were frustrated. He was jealously alert lest foreigners become acquainted with historical documents whose publication was not permitted and take them out of the country. Relative to this matter he had more than one encounter with various persons, especially with A. L. Schlözer in 1764.

Summoned from abroad to educate the children of Academician G. F. Miller, Schlözer had not gotten on well with the latter, but became a partisan of Councillor Taubert, who made him an adjunct of the academy. Later he was recommended to be the tutor of the children of the president of the academy, Count Razumovsky. In 1764 Schlözer requested leave to go abroad. At the same time he presented to the chancellery of the academy a plan for studying Russian history and an article on ancient Russian history based upon Greek sources. When he read this, Lomonosov came to the conclusion that it must not be printed. He therefore informed the senate that Taubert had entrusted the entire library to Schlözer so that he could make copies of whatever he wished, and he was now about to take excerpts abroad and publish there historical information which should not be released.

The senate decided not to grant leave to Schlözer and to take the notes away from him. This decision was not carried out in time, and therefore the senate, on Lomonosov's proposal, authorized the president of the academy to make an inquiry. Count Razumovsky was not at all pleased with this and asked Lomonosov why he had made a report to the senate and not to him, the president. Lomonosov lost no time in replying. Pointing to the series of illegalities perpetrated at the time of Schlözer's appointment to the service, he declared that, on the one hand, the matter could not brook delay, and on the other, "during your excellency's term of office here my representations to you, which were in the interest of the entire nation and for the correction of the condition of the academy, have been put into effect in a very dilatory fashion, and indeed some have received no action at all. . . ." At long last, in the autumn of 1764 Schlözer was refused the requested leave.

We now turn to Lomonosov's labors on the evolution of the Russian language and of Russian literature. As we know, the knowledge of reading and writing came to Russia at about the end of the tenth or the beginning of the eleventh century in the form of books in Church Slavonic, a language then understood by the people but not native to it since the spoken Russian language differed from Church Slavonic even in that distant time in words, expressions, and grammatical forms. This Russian language in course of time penetrated more and more into the written language and laid its stamp upon it. We find it in the *Russian Law*, in the *Tale of Igor's Raid*, in documents and the *Code of Laws*, in the *Tale of Woe-Misfortune*, and in other memorials of Russian literature. Gradually, partly under the influence of the Church Slavonic, it developed, its forms were perfected, and it became enriched by new words and turns of speech. As for the Church Slavonic, which even at that time had long been a "dead" language, a language of books and church services, it lost its purity little by little: words, grammatical forms, and turns of speech which were borrowed from the Russian language appeared in it in abundance, so that in the seventeenth century it became a mixture of the Church Slavonic and Russian languages.

Then began the seventeenth century, in Russian history so rich in events and revolutions. The Russian language, especially in the Time of Troubles, began to be filled with foreign words and phrases, chiefly Polish and Latin. In the epoch of reorganization the struggle with the old order finds sharp expression in the Russian language: it became filled with barbarisms and often presented a variegated mixture of ancient Russian words, Church Slavonic, and many foreign words—Dutch, German, French, English, and others. The absence of rules of spelling and the complete arbitrariness of syntax frequently made it monstrous. Such was the condition of the Russian language in the first quarter of the eighteenth century.

Certain writers of this period, Kantemir and Tredyakovsky, made attempts to define the relation of the different elements which formed the language and to evolve a new, purer, Russian literary language; but their attempts met with no success. Nor was much contributed by the Russian assembly founded at the Academy of Sciences in 1735, which had as its goal "to care for the perfection, the purity, and the beauty of the Russian language." For the creation of a written Russian language suitable for expressing the widest possible range of ideas, a genius was needed—and this genius was Lomonosov.

As early as 1739 he sent to the academy from Marburg an ode on the taking of Khotin (vd. Chapter 2) written in tonic verses. This ode may be considered the first production in a pure Russian language. Here Lomonosov replaced the heavy and incomprehensible language of Tredyakovsky with one incomparably more delicate and clear.[2]

The path which Lomonosov followed in the transformation of the literary language may be summed up, in its main features, in this way: first of all, he defined the interrelation of the Russian and the Church Slavonic languages and strictly differentiated one from the other; then he tried to free the Russian language from the barbarisms and the superfluous foreign words which had accumulated in it, and enriched it with new words from the popular language. His new words were fully comprehensible to a Russian and corresponded wholly to the spirit and character of our national language. Thus the Russian language did not lose its own peculiar features but became richer and more beautiful. Lomonosov fully understood this and wrote as early as 1739: "I cannot rejoice enough at the fact that our Russian language is not only not inferior to the Greek, the Latin, and the German in vigor and heroic sonority but also like them

[2] Here follow in the original text stanzas from Tredyakovsky's *Ode on the Surrender of Danzig* (1734) and from Lomonosov's *Ode on the Taking of Khotin* for comparison. ED.

is capable of versification, but with its own natural and peculiar genius."

Yet at the same time he never sought to exclude everything foreign from the language; he did not scruple to use foreign expressions for concepts for which there were no corresponding terms in Russian. This is especially true of the Russian scientific language, which he also instituted, as I have said earlier. Lomonosov also made a distinction between dialects of localities or provinces, as of Kholmogory or Moscow. From these he set the Moscow dialect as the standard of the Russian language since it was "justly preferred not only for the importance of the capital city but also for its superior beauty."

Later, in his article *On the Use of Church Books in the Russian Language* (printed in 1757) he expounded in full his ideas and views on the interrelation of the Russian and Church Slavonic tongues. He sees in the latter a foundation for the Russian language in the sense that it would provide both a source of new words and a framework of grammatical rules. In his opinion only the man who had studied the Church Slavonic books in detail could be able to write Russian correctly. Only after a close acquaintance with these books could one learn to distinguish common or "low" words—that is, colloquial, ordinary words of which the Russian language is largely composed—from the elevated words common to the Russian and Slavonic languages, and from the Slavonic, words comprehensible to Russians.

He made a threefold division of styles of diction: the high, made up of Slavonic-Russian and Slavonic "expressions" comprehensible to Russians; the middle, made up mainly of Russian expressions, to which it was possible to add Slavonic ones, appropriate to the subject treated and such that the style should not seem bombastic; and the low, composed of purely Russian words, such as could not be found in the church books. In this way "Wild and strange words, absurd words, which have come to us from strange languages, will be turned away, and the Russian language will be maintained in its full force, beauty, and richness, not subject to changes and decay, as long as the Russian church shall be beautified by glorifying God in the Slavonic tongue."

At first glance a purely formal division into three "styles," this division exercised a most beneficial influence on Russian literature, giving in the last, or third, style, broad access to literature in the common colloquial Russian language, which up to that time had been generally considered objectionable for literary use.

Lomonosov himself constantly showed during the whole course of his life how to put his theoretical degrees of diction into practice. Models of all "styles" can be found in his works. In his eulogistic speeches we see the "high" style; many speeches and articles of a scientific character are written in the middle style; finally, the lower style may be seen in his letters, reports, and notes. At the present time his high style, and partly too the middle one, seem inflated and unnatural, while, on the contrary, his low style is marked by force and expressiveness. Undoubtedly, Lomonosov exaggerated the importance of the Church-Slavonic language for the Russian, but his views were distinctly advanced for his time.

Indispensable for the Russian language were, moreover, the rules of spelling in his *Russian Grammar*, which appeared in 1755 after long and painstaking work. This is the first Russian grammar, for until then there were only grammars of the Church Slavonic language. Russian was not studied specially since it was considered vulgar. In this grammar are found for the first time examples collected from the popular language which illustrate the rules of speech united into a harmonious system. Lomonosov's *Rus-*

sian Grammar falls into six divisions, or precepts as he calls them. The first precept, "on human speech in general," treats broader questions of philology. The second precept, "on Russian reading and spelling," gives a short explanation of phonetics and the rules of writing, very valuable for that time for their exactness and clear definition. The third precept, "of the noun," deals with the formation of words and the declension of substantives, adjectives, and numerals. The fourth precept, "of the verb," gives a classification of Russian verbs of the first and second conjugations and abundant examples and models of conjugation. The fifth precept has to do with the remaining parts of speech. The sixth precept compactly expounds questions of syntax.

Throughout the grammar Lomonosov for the first time makes use of the empirical method of observing the language, advances many examples from the colloquial speech, and in difficult cases advises that moot points be decided according to the results of concrete observations and comparisons from the living speech. He strictly separates the Church Slavonic elements from the purely Russian. Many of Lomonosov's observations have retained their importance even down to our day. His grammar was one of the most advanced of his era, and for more than a century (until the appearance of the grammar of A. Kh. Vostokov in 1831) was the only work of this type in the Russian language. During Lomonosov's life and after his death the grammar was published eleven times and was translated into German, French, and even into modern Greek.

Equally important was Lomonosov's role in the founding of the Russian scientific language. This language, which did not begin to appear in Russia until the time of Peter the Great, represents almost exclusively borrowings from foreign sources: each specialist made use of German, Dutch, Polish, and Latin words to signify technical objects—words which were incomprehensible to others.[3] A many-sided knowledge of the Russian language, broad information in the exact sciences, and an excellent acquaintance with Latin, Greek, and the Western European languages, reinforced by his literary talent and native genius, enabled Lomonosov to lay correct foundations for Russian technical and scientific terminology. The basic theses to which he held, and other Russian scholars after him, unfortunately seem to be unknown to our contemporaries:

(a) it is necessary to translate foreign scientific words into the Russian language;

(b) words should be left untranslated only in cases where it is not possible to find a fully equivalent Russian word, or when the foreign word has become generally known;

(c) in such cases give the foreign word a form more closely related to the Russian language.

A great many of the scientific expressions in Russian

[3] "Who for example could guess that:

Teken (German, *Zeichen**)	means	sketch (drawing)
Kianka (?)	"	mallet
Ber (German, *Wehr*)	"	dam (weir)
Dak (German, *Dach*)	"	roof
Cordon (French)	"	cord, string

Little by little chemical terms began to appear which were also completely incomprehensible, such as:

Lavra (English, laurel)	means	indigo blue (highest quality)
Tir (German, *Teer*)	"	liquid tar
Shpiauter (English, Spelter)	"	zinc (used in this day in industry)

and scientific terms, such as:

Perpendikul (Latin)	means	pendulum
Radix (Latin)	"	root
Triangul (Latin)	"	triangle
Kentr (Latin)	"	center
Additsia (Latin)	"	addition"

* Foreign sources suggested by the Editor.

which Lomonosov himself coined in conformity with these rules are used by all of us.[4]

Lomonosov's scientific and technical words and expressions gradually displaced earlier awkward terms, and at the end of his life he was able to see with satisfaction the extent to which the Russian language had become purified of various types of barbarisms. He refers to this in his petition for retirement in 1762: "As a result of my compositions of various kinds in the indigenous language, grammatical, rhetorical, poetical, historical, and those which belong to the higher sciences—that is, the physical, chemical, and mechanical—the Russian style during the past twenty years has become incomparably purer than before and much more capable of expressing difficult ideas. To this stands witness the general approbation of my works and the words and expressions used in written documents of every kind—a situation which serves much for the enlightenment of the people." Lomonosov laid the foundation of the exact Russian scientific language without which no one could get along today.

In Lomonosov's poetic works the language is very much freer, more elegant, and more perfect than in the eulogistic speeches and dissertations, and in his poetry the musical side of Russian speech is clearly in evidence. It need hardly be said that until his time a musical Russian poetry did not exist.[5]

Certainly, Lomonosov did not neglect the theory of prose and poetry. His *Rhetoric* was devoted to prose and was the first such work in the Russian tongue. It is not a completely independent composition and was chiefly important for the numerous examples which demonstrate the beauty and

[4] Here follows in the Russian original a list of scientific and laboratory terms in common use. ED.

[5] Here follows in the Russian original an example of his musical quality, lines from his translation of Anacreon. ED.

strength of the Russian language. He zealously evolved a theory of poetry not in textbooks but in beautiful compositions of his own. Precisely speaking, the only thing he wrote on the theory of poetry was the letter from Marburg (1739) on the rules of Russian versification in which he emphasized the necessity of substituting quantitative meter for the syllabic meter, which was so foreign to the spirit of the Russian language. Tredyakovsky was the first to propose quantitative verse in his *Method of Composing Russian Verses* (1735), but at the time the method won no followers—probably because Tredyakovsky's examples were not very convincing since he himself did not cease to write syllabic verse after 1735. In his letter Lomonosov criticized Tredyakovsky's *Method* and introduced numerous emendations which were later accepted. Lomonosov's reform was made on truly national principles since the quantitative method had been used in popular songs for a long time. But his reform became widespread not, indeed, because of his *Rules of Russian Versification* since it was not published until after his death in 1778, but because he gave numerous examples of versification in the quantitative method in his own works, and actually showed in this way how much better this form was than the syllabic.

Lomonosov's poetical works (with the exception of the eulogistic odes) may be examined only in connection with his other activities. We have already seen ample evidence that Lomonosov was first of all a sincere investigator of nature who constantly saw before him great and inexplicable natural phenomena. A poet at heart, he went into poetic rapture over the same phenomena which he studied with most searching interest as a naturalist. This is why in Lomonosov's poetry we almost never find pictures of nature, of her moods and beauties, but rather natural phenomena. His best-known and most poetic work, *Morning and Evening Meditations on the Majesty of God* (Chapter 2) demonstrate this excellently. Here we have before us the sincere poetic feeling of the naturalist meditating on solar phenomena and on the nature of the northern lights, and clothing in a poetic form, in conformity with the general spirit of the period, his perplexities, queries, and conjectures. Lomonosov's poetry is in many cases typical poetry of natural science. And in a like way the circumstances of Lomonosov's life explain his transpositions of those particular psalms which deal predominantly with cruel implacable hatred for enemies.

With Lomonosov his eulogistic works, and especially his solemn odes, occupy a special position. Today odes of this kind seem turgid and unnatural; they are essentially glorification of personages, praise of Russia, of famous events. But in Lomonosov's time such odes were in favor and it was part of the duty of the academicians to compose them even as it was their duty to set up fireworks and illuminations. Lomonosov worked out for his odes a separate style, a special model according to which they were composed, and thus they are all somewhat alike. He created his own literary school, his own literary tendency; his followers quite often borrowed not only his methods but his very language.

Although he had acquired nobility by his rank, Lomonosov always set the interests of the Russian people before all else and always upheld them as much as possible in his poems, which often contain his favorite ideas on the development and diffusion of culture and enlightenment for the general good of the people. A fine example of this occurs in a well-known passage in the ode to the day of Elizabeth Petrovna's accession to the throne, a passage devoted to the education of youth:

> O you, whom eagerly awaits
> Our fatherland from out its silent depths,
> Seeking among its sons trained minds
> Like those it now must bring from alien lands. . . .

(1747)

Later, as a scholar and as a natural philosopher and a naturalist, he could not refrain from mentioning the sciences in his odes, and the resultant verses are distinguished by a fervor, a sincerity of feeling, seldom encountered in works of this genre. Here he is a propagandist making use of the odes for the diffusion of enlightenment, as is shown for example by the following excerpts:

> O sciences felicitous and
> Diligent, stretch forth your hands
> And survey to the farthest lands.
> Traverse the earth and ocean's deeps,
> Wide steppes and densest forest. . . .
> Everywhere and every hour explore
> All that is beautiful and great—
> Things that the world has not yet seen;
> Amaze the ages by your works,
> As far as in you lies show forth
> By the gracious bounty of Elizabeth. . . .
> Thou, Chemistry, do penetrate
> With vision keen the bowels of the earth,
> Reveal what treasure Russia hides there. . . .
> Science of flashing meteors
> Foretell the changes in the heavens,
> And stormy atmospheric arguments
> By signs dependable forecast.

And this is the picture Lomonosov conceived of the students hastening to the university in St. Petersburg:

> And there shall come to us success in teaching
> And glorious fame when this, Thy University,
> Shall flourish in Thy name wherever shines the sun,
> Embellished by Thy gifts, eternally just
> For the true splendor of the Russian State.
> And youth shall flock to us from everywhere
> To give themselves to learning here in Peter's town.
>
> (Verses in petition to Empress Elizabeth Petrovna, 1761)

And then we frequently find in Lomonosov, alongside eulogies of kings, indications of their lacks, of their actions harmful to the people, and sometimes a critical attitude toward the behavior of ruling personages.

Under the existing conditions it is understandable that Lomonosov could not express his thoughts and views in the press. Hence we find them in odes, where it was possible to point out to the rulers (first acknowledging them as possessed of those qualities which he wished to see in them) those ideals toward which they should strive in order to "make their people happy." These ideals were expressed with increasing boldness as Lomonosov's position grew stronger, so that he found in odes an effective weapon for his activity as a publicist. He is the first Russian to use verses in this fashion for propaganda purposes.

Here are some appropriate excerpts from various odes:

> These things to you the Lord imparts . . .
> To righteous services adhere,
> To widows, orphans, pity show;
> Be friend unto the truthful hearts
> And to the poor a shield sincere;
> In faithfulness maintain your word,
> Goodwill to others undeterred;
> To suppliants open wide the gate;
> Comfort to sufferers accord,
> To laborers their decreed reward,
> And Peter's daughter contemplate.
>
> (On the birthday of Empress Elizabeth Petrovna, 1757)

> Then earthly Judges, give you pause,
> And all the reigning heads of lands;
> You should preserve the sacred laws
> From breach by careless, violent hands;
> Your subjects you should not despise—
> Correct their vices in this wise;
> By labor, teaching, gentleness.

Let mercy and justice jointly reign;
The people's privileges maintain;
And then the Lord your house will bless.

(On the day of the accession to the throne
of Empress Catherine II, July 28, 1762)

. . . the Goddess speaks;
I do ascend my Father's throne
Th'oppressed from evil to release,
And by a liberal rule to own
My Breed, and learned men increase,
Under my reign, restrained might
Scorns punishment by death as night,
I'll rule more quietly than zephyr.

(On the day of the accession to the throne
of Empress Elizabeth Petrovna, 1761)

The patriot heroes speak of their brethren:

Death we would welcome for the Goddess,
Who to the dead has given life,
Has freed condemned men from their prison,
And graciously raised up the poor,
Pouring courage into the nation.

(On the name day of Empress Elizabeth Petrovna, 1759)

Finally, there appear constantly in these odes echoes of
and allusions to political events of the time. These cannot
always be identified since we, of course, do not know everything that then disturbed and alarmed the upper classes of
society.

A singular sort of composition in which Lomonosov was
obliged to engage as part of his duties was the composition
of descriptions of the illuminations with which the Academy
of Sciences marked its festival days. These illuminations
were arranged on a raised wooden platform constructed on
the Neva opposite the academy. Some were depicted in
copper engravings. Here is Lomonosov's description of one

of these illuminations, which was arranged on September 5, 1752, in honor of the name day of Elizabeth Petrovna.

"To be represented in perspective was a landing place strengthened by two dikes which extended into the sea: at the end of the landing place, looking toward the sea, to be depicted a mighty colossus standing with its feet on the ends of the dikes. With his right hand he raises the initials in capitals of the name of Her Imperial Majesty; with the left, he holds a flaming bright torch. Within the landing place is to be set, on the right side, the temple of Peace; on the left side, the temple of Plenty, with the marks and embellishments appertaining thereto. The colossus can perhaps be most conveniently depicted on canvas—but all the rest outlined in lanterns. The significance of this symbolic depiction is briefly contained in the following verses:"

> Once the great island Race, who wished to save
> From gale and storm those drifting on the wave,
> To give to others comfort, and win praise,
> A wondrous structure on the shore did raise.
> A mighty giant, seventy ells high, all night
> Above the giant swell would hold a light.
> Far o'er the restless sea its beam would pour
> And led the periled vessels safe to shore.
> Give rest to all, O Empress, by Thy name;
> Like to a giant, tall as stars, Thy fame
> The universe illumines with Thy worth,
> Fills with Thy name the ocean and the earth.
> Save us from storm; Elizabeth will guarantee
> Gladly our rest and comfort in tranquillity.

Concerning Lomonosov's appraisal of his poetry Pushkin says: "Lomonosov himself did not set great value on his poetry and was more concerned about his chemical experiments than about the obligatory odes on a name day of a royal personage or the like. How scornfully he speaks of

Sumarokov, who was passionate about his art, 'that man, who thinks of nothing but his own poor versifying. . . .' On the other hand with what fire he speaks of the sciences, of enlightenment!"

Lomonosov's literary pursuits put him in constant contact with contemporary poets and writers, of which the greatest were held to be A. P. Sumarokov and V. Tredyakovsky, the latter an academician in the chair of eloquence. The mutual relationship of these men were quite characteristic of the time. Lomonosov had been friendly with Sumarokov at one time but later a rift occurred between them. When they became representatives of different schools of political thought, their mutual hostility became the more bitter. Sumarokov contributed his verses to the magazine *Monthly Compositions*, issued by the Academy of Sciences under the editorship of Academician Miller. In 1759 Sumarokov founded his own magazine, *The Industrious Bee*, which was printed on the academy press. That made it possible for Lomonosov to interfere with the affairs of the journal; supported by the president, he refused to permit the publication of Sumarokov's *Absurd Odes*—parodies of Lomonosov's odes—in *The Industrious Bee*. It goes without saying that Sumarokov was very much offended by this interference and wrote to Shuvalov that "It is impossible for me to submit any more of my works to the nation, for Lomonosov stops them . . . he acts the worst sort of villain, lest I disclose his great ignorance in literary sciences to the whole world; and nearly all at the academy fear him and seek to please him against their will."

Shuvalov frequently called the two men to him, and on these occasions they usually criticized the most recent works, quarreled about Russian grammar, the advantages of a certain meter of verse, and the like. In Timkovsky's words, the angrier Sumarokov became the more Lomonosov taunted him, and often, if the quarrel became exceptionally heated,

Shuvalov dismissed either Sumarokov or both of them. If Lomonosov became carried away by his complaints, then Shuvalov sent for Sumarokov and at the same time started a conversation about him. The latter, learning that Lomonosov was present, either went away or, having eavesdropped, ran in with the cry, "Do not believe him, your excellency." A letter written by Lomonosov on January 19, 1761, following attempts by Shuvalov to conciliate them, has been preserved: "No one has insulted me in my life as your excellency has. Today you summoned me to you. I thought there might be some sort of satisfaction awaiting me in accord with my justified requests. All of a sudden I hear: Make peace with Sumarokov, that is, commit a joke and infamy. . . . I forget all his malevolence and have no desire to take revenge in any way, and God has not given me an evil heart. But I am not able in any way to make friends and get along with him, knowing and having experienced in many cases what a sharp nettle he is. . . . Not wishing to offend you by refusing in the presence of so many gentlemen, I showed you obedience; but, I assure you, it is for the last time . . . ; to treat with such a person I cannot and do not desire—a man who defames all other branches of learning whose spirit he does not comprehend. And this is my sincere opinion which I now present to you without any sort of anger. I do not wish to be a court fool at the table of eminent lords or of such earthly rulers, nor even of the Lord God himself, who gave me my wit, until perchance he takes it away. . . . If the diffusion of learning in Russia is dear to you, if my zeal toward you has not vanished from your memory, endeavor quickly to fulfill my requests, which are justified for the benefit of our land, but forget about my reconciliation with Sumarokov as a petty thing. . . ."

Academician Stählin relates the following incident in his memoirs: "Kammerherr[6] Shuvalov once invited many schol-

[6] Court title meaning chamberlain. ED.

ars to dine with him, according to his custom, and among their number Lomonosov and Sumarokov. Before two o'clock the guests, all gathered and ready to sit down at the table, awaited only the arrival of Lomonosov, who, not knowing that Sumarokov had been invited, did not appear until about two o'clock. Having come about halfway across the room and suddenly noticing Sumarokov among the guests, he immediately turned around and, without uttering a word, walked back to the door in order to retire. The Kammerherr cried out to him, 'Where are you going, Mik- hailo Vasilyevich? We are just sitting down to table and were only waiting for you.' 'Home,' replied Lomonosov, already holding on to the catch of the open door. 'But why?' exclaimed the Kammerherr, 'You know I invited you to dine with me.' 'For the reason,' answered Lomonosov, 'that I do not wish to dine with fools.' Here he pointed at Sumar- okov and left the room."

Accounting himself the greatest Russian poet, Sumarokov in the *Russian Parnassus* only briefly mentions Lomonosov and N. Popovsky (Lomonosov's pupil in versification and later professor at the University of Moscow) and says that, in his merits, "Mr. Lomonosov is as far removed from Tredyakovsky as heaven from hell"; he advises writers to imitate "this honorable man in the beauty of his lyricism" but to remember that "verses without pure prosody are easy labor and the most niggardly prose." He saw in Lomonosov a true poet, but one harmed by a careless regard for the external form of verse.

With another poet of the day, Professor of Rhetoric V. K. Tredyakovsky, Lomonosov had begun to have hostile relations as early as 1741 as a consequence of his criticisms of Tredyakovsky's opinions, criticisms made in connection with the laws of Russian versification which he wrote at Marburg. These hostilities ceased only with Tredyakovsky's dismissal from the academy in 1759. The subjects of the quarrels and discords between them were most varied. For instance, in the course of several sessions of the conference in 1746 a dispute went on regarding the nominative case ending of plural adjectives of the masculine gender. Tredyakovsky thought that the correct ending was "i," but Lomonosov maintained it to be "e," as is accepted today. Lomonosov also exchanged epigrams and satires with Tredyakovsky just as he did with Sumarokov.

CHAPTER 8

A short history of the conduct of the chancellery of the academy. . . .—The new organization of the academy—The last letter to his fatherland—Lomonosov's illness and death—The fate of his papers—His appearance and character—An appraisal of his accomplishment: Lomonosov as a scholar—His relations with Euler—Lomonosov as a spreader of enlightenment and a statesman.

I N 1764 Lomonosov's illness, which had brought him almost to the grave in 1762 and early 1763, set in again, one symptom of it being open sores on his painfully swollen legs. During this year his encounters with other academicians as well as with the leader of the chancellery, I. K. Taubert, were especially sharp. One of these, which involved A. L. Schlözer, has already been discussed. Lomonosov wrote, probably in either July or August of 1764, *A Short History of the Conduct of the Chancellery of the Academy in Respect of Learned Persons and Affairs from the Beginning of this Body up to the Present Time.* Its seventy-one paragraphs contain a detailed description of the unseemly behavior of the directors of the chancellery, I. K. Schumacher and his worthy successor, Taubert, and their many attempts to hinder the spread of learning in Russia by which, in one way or another, they prevented the realization of Lomonosov's plans. This *History* closes with some characteristic assertions: "Meanwhile learning is subjected to every conceivable obstacle. . . . The only hope now lies in our most gracious sovereign, who, from sincere love of learning and zeal for the improvement of our native land, will perhaps observe these woes and avert them. But if this does not come to pass, then one must believe it is not God's will that learning should grow and spread in Russia." The following note, written in one of his papers,

shows Lomonosov's own condition: "I suffer because I try
to defend the work of Peter the Great so that the Russians
may learn and show their worth. I do not grieve over death;
I have lived and suffered, and I know that the children of
the fatherland will mourn over me."

A second great work, composed perhaps somewhat earlier
than the *Short History* but pursuing the same goal (to better the position of the academicians in the academy and
make it possible for them to carry out successfully the fundamental task of serving the interests of education and of
Russia) was his project for a new statute for the Academy
of Sciences. This project, written at the suggestion of the
president, is a voluminous work bearing the title, A *New
Institution and Establishment of the St. Petersburg Imperial
Academy of Sciences, written for the Imperial scrutiny and
approval.* In it a new division of the classes of the academy
is presented, a number of new subjects are introduced, and
new chairs established. So that the academy might become
a purely Russian institution as soon as there were sufficient
qualified scholars among us, all academicians must be na-
tive-born Russians. Foremost of their duties must be promotion of the general welfare of Russia. The chancellery of
the academy was made a subordinate agency, the administration of the academy was placed in the hands of the
academicians themselves, and all departments of arts and
handicrafts were abolished.

This project was sent in the name of the conference of
the academy to Count G. G. Orlov to be presented for
confirmation by Catherine II. With it went a letter from
Lomonosov in which he pointed out that the entire project
was designed solely for "the true benefit of learning in
Russia in order that it might be more quickly disseminated
for the increased well-being of the loyal subjects of Her
Imperial Majesty, and to overcome all previous difficulties
that had burdened learning." He requested that the project

be presented to the empress as quickly as possible and even drafted the text for an appropriate ukase. But at that time the proposed statute received no approval. However, much that Lomonosov considered necessary was introduced after his death.

At the beginning of the next year, 1765, Catherine issued a ukase which admitted A. L. Schlözer to service as academician and professor of history, bestowed upon him all privileges of academicians of long standing, and granted him a large stipend. Further, in order that his works "could be produced in print unhampered, it was permitted him, as testimony of his zeal, to present them most respectfully to Her Imperial Majesty"—that is, over the head of the conference of the academy. Lomonosov, who was beside himself, had the temerity to write a sharp criticism of the separate points of the contract entitled, *Consequences of the Appointment of Schlözer as Ordinary Professor of History*. This note had no consequences whatsoever either for Schlözer or for Lomonosov.

As Lomonosov's illness progressed his irritability increased and his opinions on various events were expressed with even greater vehemence than before. More than once in the course of the first months of this year he wrangled with Academician G. F. Miller, who had received an appointment in Moscow, and even with his own pupil, S. Ya. Rumovsky, who in Lomonosov's opinion had become an oppressor of learning and a friend of Taubert.

But a letter of March 2, 1765, the last he wrote to his sister, who still lived in the place of his childhood, was filled with entirely different sentiments: "My lady Marya Vasilyevna, congratulations on your many years with your husband and children. I am very pleased to report that Mishenka arrived in St. Petersburg in good health and that he can read very well and correctly, and also writes excellently for a child. Immediately on his arrival new French clothes were made for him, with sewn shirts, and he was dressed from head to foot; and he trims his hair in our fashion, so that they wouldn't know him at Matigory. The most surprising thing to me is that he is not bashful and immediately became accustomed to us and to our cooking as if he had lived with us a hundred years; he has given no sign of lonesomeness or weeping. The day before yesterday I sent him to the school of the Academy of Sciences here, which is under my direction, where forty children of nobles and commoners are being instructed. Here he will live and study under good supervision, and on holidays and Sundays he will dine, sup, and spend the night at home with me. I have ordered that he be taught the Latin tongue, arithmetic, to write clearly and prettily, and to dance. Yesterday I spent much of the evening at the school with the purpose of observing how he has supper with the scholars in the commons and with whom he shares a room. Believe me, dear sister, that I take pains on his account as a good uncle and godfather should. My wife and daughter also love him and provide him with everything. I have no doubt that he will be happy in his schooling, and I remain, with sincere affection, your brother, Mikhailo Lomonosov."

In the middle of March Lomonosov caught cold and took to his bed; he became increasingly worse, and died on April 4, 1765. His friend, Academician Yakov Yakovlevich Stählin, was with him almost constantly through his last days, and has preserved many characteristic facts from Lomonosov's life for us. All of St. Petersburg was present at the solemn funeral rites. Stählin tells us that Sumarokov came up to him when he was one of the pallbearers, pointed at the deceased lying in the coffin, and said, "The fool has become silent and can make no more noise." Stählin answered, "I would not have advised you to say that to him when he was alive." Lomonosov inspired such fear in Sumarokov that he did not dare to open his mouth in his presence.

Lomonosov is buried in the Lazarus cemetery of the Alexander Nevsky monastery in Leningrad. On his grave a monument of white marble was placed by Count M. L. Vorontsov, his patron of long standing, with an inscription composed by Stählin and a design also made by him. His admirer, Count A. P. Shuvalov, wrote an ode in French in which he paid due honor to Lomonosov's worth.

All papers found in Lomonosov's house were sealed immediately after his death by Count G. G. Orlov on the order of Catherine II. Later Orlov took possession of the greater part, while the remainder was returned to his wife and daughter. Evidently all papers removed by Orlov had some sort of government significance. To this day their place of concealment remains unknown. On the other hand, Lomonosov's scientific works and notes apparently had no interest for Orlov, and have, fortunately, been preserved for us. After the revolution the archive of the Academy of Sciences took upon itself the task of collecting as many of Lomonosov's manuscripts as possible. At the present time everything found in the different institutions of the Academy of Sciences has been concentrated in this archive. Some of the papers were donated to the archive by E. N. Orlova, Lomonosov's great-granddaughter. There are 948 manuscripts in all. At present further search for papers which may still be in the possession of private persons is under way, and an effort is being made to have all of his manuscripts now in other government institutions turned over to the archives of the academy. Such a concentration of all of Lomonosov's manuscripts in one place is indispensable to the publication of a complete collection of his works, an undertaking already begun by the Academy of Sciences.

This biography may well be closed by bringing together certain interesting facts about Lomonosov which were preserved by Academician Stählin, some of Alexander Push-

kin's penetrating opinions of the man, and a brief appraisal
of his achievements in certain fields of labor.

"Lomonosov was distinguished for his physical vigor and
athletic strength. While adjunct of the academy, he lived
on Vasilyevsky Island . . . and had little acquaintance with
other people. Once, on a beautiful autumn evening, he went
out alone for a walk along Grand Avenue on the island,
toward the sea. On the way back, as he walked in the
gathering darkness through the part of the boulevard that
was hacked out of the woods, three sailors suddenly jumped
from the bushes and fell upon him. There was not another
soul in the neighborhood. With the utmost bravery he
defended himself against the three brigands. One he struck
such a blow that it knocked him unconscious to the ground.
To the second he delivered a powerful blow in the face, and
the rogue, covered with blood, ran as fast as he could back
into the bushes. Then, as the first regained consciousness
and fled to the woods, it was not difficult for Lomonosov
to overcome the third. Throwing him to the ground and
holding him between his legs, he threatened to kill him on
the spot unless he disclosed the names of the two other
bandits and the reason for their attack. The rogue confessed
that they only wanted to rob him and then let him go. 'Ah,
canaille,' said Lomonosov, 'then I will rob you.' And the
thief then and there had to remove his jacket, his sackcloth
shirt, and breeches, roll them into a bundle, and fasten it
with his own belt. Then, striking the half-naked sailor once
more on the legs so that he fell to the ground, hardly able
to move from the spot, Lomonosov put the bundle on his
shoulder and proceeded homeward with his booty."

Pushkin had an excellent understanding of Lomonosov's
character. "Everywhere he was exactly the same: at home,
where everybody trembled before him; at court, where he
pulled the pages by the ears; in the academy, where, on
Schlözer's testimony, they dared not utter a word in his

presence. . . . Born in lowly rank, he had no ambition to elevate himself by effrontery and familiarity with persons of higher station. But he could stand on his own feet and he did not overvalue the patronage of his Maecenases when it was a question of his honor or of the triumph of his favorite ideas. Listen to what he writes to Shuvalov: 'Not only do I not wish to be a court fool at the table of lords and such earthly rulers, but even of the Lord God himself, who gave me my wit until he sees fit to take it away' " (January 19, 1761). Withal Lomonosov was fully aware of his own superiority in science to many of the contemporary academicians, the majority of whom (in contrast to the ones first called from abroad, such as Bernoulli and Euler) were only commonplace scholars. And this superiority he more than once expressed directly and openly; for example, in the letter of December 30, 1754, to Shuvalov already cited (Chapter 4) and in his petition for retirement (1762) he says that, "I have adorned the Academy of Sciences before the whole world for twenty years." And in 1764 he began to write his *Conspectus of the Most Important Theorems with which Mikhail Lomonosov has Enriched Science*, which he intended to present to the Paris Academy of Sciences.

He was truly a sincere scholar, ready to give up everything for learning. This side of his character, too, was cogently expressed by Pushkin, who had evidently made a thorough study of Lomonosov's works. "Combining unusual will power with an unusual power of comprehension, Lomonosov embraced all the branches of knowledge. The thirst for learning was the strongest passion of this passion-filled soul. Historian, rhetorician, mechanician, chemist, mineralogist, artist, and poet—he scrutinized and fathomed everything."

Today we value Lomonosov primarily as an outstanding philosopher and thinker. While still a student, he divined the basic theme of investigation which was most of all to further the development of physics and chemistry: the study of the minute particles of which all bodies are composed and of their properties. Connecting all phenomena with the properties of the particles which make up matter, he himself came to some remarkable conclusions and foretold the general conditions and paths of the development of both physics and chemistry down to our time. In many other sciences, too, he expressed extremely important ideas which were not proved to be correct until many years later. His many-sided genius made itself felt everywhere, and in everything he was years, decades, or a century ahead of his time.

A consequence of this was that he could not bring his remarkably vast projects to actual completion. The stage of development of the sciences in the middle eighteenth century by no means corresponded to the lofty demands which Lomonosov made upon them. There was neither the requisite apparatus nor even hints as to the method of those researches which he wished to undertake. He did what he could himself—he invented a multitude of new apparatus, a multitude of methods which were new for the time—but of course he could not accomplish everything alone. If information had been preserved for us of all the new devices and instruments which were constantly born in his head and ordered to be built by the workmen of the academy and later by his own craftsmen, then we should have an amazing gallery of Lomonosov's inventions.

A second consequence was the fact that almost none of his contemporaries, even the academicians, could understand what he did or appreciate it at its true value. That, we are barely able to do today, after a century and a half or more. Not grasping the significance of his work in chemistry and physics, they thought it not worth special attention. During Lomonosov's life, so far as we can judge, there was only one man who appreciated him fully, who understood all the significance of what he did, who was initiated into all the details of his scientific thought. This was the famous mathematician, Academician Leonhard Euler, and I think it necessary to devote a few words here to their relations, which undoubtedly exercised no small influence on the development of Lomonosov's creative activity in science.

Leonhard Euler, a member of the Academy of Sciences since 1727, probably saw Lomonosov when the latter was a student of the university of the academy in 1736. Then, we know that Euler on May 4, 1739, read Lomonosov's dissertation which was sent from Marburg and that he left St. Petersburg three days before Lomonosov returned from abroad. We know also that Euler returned to St. Petersburg a year after Lomonosov died, in 1766, and remained there until his own death, September 7, 1783. Thus after 1736 they could not have seen each other. Their correspondence began at the beginning of 1748, after Euler had sent to the academy very good reports on Lomonosov's first dissertations. Later he asked that Lomonosov be urged to write a work in competition for the prize offered by the Berlin Academy of Sciences in 1749 on the subject, *The Production and Composition of Saltpeter*. (This Lomonosov did, but he did not receive the prize.)

In his letters Euler always speaks well of Lomonosov's gifts and praises his works. He retained the same good opinion of him even after the latter in 1755, without Euler's knowledge, published one of his letters in the magazine *Caméléon Littéraire*, then appearing in St. Petersburg. The Seven Years' War, which broke out in the following year, interrupted their correspondence when Euler and Lomonosov found themselves in countries at war with each other. The last letter which Lomonosov received from Euler was in the year 1761 and was written in connection with the following incident. When on October 18, 1760, the Russian troops occupied Berlin and Russian officers were quartered in Euler's house, he was obliged to pay an indemnity, thereby suffering losses amounting to 1,200 rubles. Euler, as an honorary member of the Russian Academy of Sciences, resolved to recover his money and asked Lomonosov to assist him in high government circles. Lomonosov took the necessary steps and Euler received his money during the reign of Catherine II.

Lomonosov constantly united with his love for the sciences the urge to propagate them as widely as possible among the Russian people. This was yet another trait of his character which Pushkin fully discerned. "Lomonosov was a great man," he says. "Between Peter I and Catherine II he was the only original champion of the Enlightenment. He founded the first university; rather, he himself was our first university." We have seen many times what steps Lomonosov took toward this end and we must accord him his just due; very few people can take credit for such a feat as the founding of a university. And although Lomonosov took no part in the work of the University of Moscow after its foundation, he did not cease to devote attention to events taking place there. It was not for nothing that his works were printed at the press of the University of Moscow from 1757 to 1759.

The older Lomonosov became, the more pronounced became his desire to educate his people—to plant culture in Russia. To G. N. Teplov, one of those who helped guide the destiny of the academy, he expressed himself with complete candor in a letter that has been preserved for us: "I should be glad to keep silent and live in peace did I not fear punishment from justice and omnipotent Providence, which has not deprived me of gifts and diligence in study and now has granted me the opportunity, and has given me endurance, noble persistence, and the boldness to surmount all obstacles to the diffusion of learning in our country, which is dearer to me than anything in my life. . . . I have consecrated myself to this work, to strive until my death with the foes of Russian learning, just as I have been struggling for twenty years; I have stood for it from my youth, and in age I will not abandon it" (January 30, 1761).

But the propagation of learning was one component part of Lomonosov's vastly broader plan by which he sought to promote the welfare of the entire Russian people. Indispensable to that end were profound economic reconstructions of the way of life prevailing in his time, and he intended to write—and probably wrote—a series of letters and reports on these themes. They have not come down to us, and we must assume that G. G. Orlov confiscated them immediately from among the papers Lomonosov left. Only a letter to Shuvalov concerning the increase of the Russian population has been preserved, but it discloses Lomonosov's basic points of view as a statesman. This over-all national scale of his activity became especially marked in the last five years of his life, when he had attained the highest degree of fame and influence and when his voice was undoubtedly listened to. "How joyful to work for the welfare of society," he says in the ode dedicated to Count Shuvalov, the inventor of new types of cannon (1760).

How correct is his opinion of his own verse as a diversion in comparison with matters dealing with the welfare of the whole nation! And yet the great majority of his contemporaries saw him only as a poet, a philologist, an orator, the founder of the Russian language. These services, of course, were tremendous, the more so as they were in the last analysis evident to all and were preserved *in toto* for posterity. Lomonosov himself confessed that his scientific innovations would have no immediate propagators among the Russians; that his efforts to do everything possible to ameliorate the condition of the people, his efforts to raise the level of culture, for the propagation of enlightenment, would find no response in the ruling class. He realized that his beloved mosaics and the glass factory, on the development of which he had expended so much strength and energy, putting forth all his genius, would cease to exist after him. All this he expressed on his death bed to Academician Stählin: "Friend, I see that I must die and I look on death peacefully and indifferently. I regret only that I was unable to bring to completion everything I undertook for the benefit of my country, for the increase of learning, and for the greater glory of the academy, and that now, at the end of my life, I realize that all of my good intentions will vanish with me."

But if Lomonosov had been able to foresee the future, he would not have given way to such somber reflections, for the projects which he began were realized sooner or later. Already during the reign of Catherine II far-reaching reforms took place for the expansion of education. The end of the eighteenth century saw the foundation of the School of Mines (now the Mining Institute) and the Academy of Medicine and Surgery, while the universities of Kharkov, Kazan, and St. Petersburg were founded at the beginning of the nineteenth century. Parallel to these, there quickly developed a network of elementary and secondary schools.

In surveying Lomonosov's scientific activity, which he always considered by far the most important aspect of his work, we have already had occasion to point out the close connection of the development of chemistry from 1790 to 1800 with those quantitative methods of research which he constantly advanced and applied. His physical chemistry was revived more than a century after his death, and in a very short time came to luxuriant flower.

And if Lomonosov were to appear among us, he would find thousands of investigators working on the theme which he always held up as basic to the understanding of matter: the study of "the insensible particles which make up substances" with the help of the methods of physics, mathematics, and chemistry. It is as if he foresaw the amazing achievements resulting from this study which promise even more glorious developments in the future. With full justice we may apply to Lomonosov himself the words of his translation from Horace:

A deathless monument I've left behind me,
Loftier than the pyramids, stronger than brass,
It cannot be erased by stormy Aquilon,
By centuries nor hoary age's gnawing.
I shall not die; but death shall leave intact
The grander part of me, when my life ends.

MENSHUTKIN'S PUBLICATIONS
ON LOMONOSOV

1904 (1) "M. V. Lomonosov Considered as a Physical Chemist" (in Russian). *Annals of the Polytechnic Institute of St. Petersburg, 1904-1905*, Vols. 1, 2, 3, 4. *Journal of the Russian Chemical Society*, Vol. 36. As a separate book, St. Petersburg, iv + 300 pages, with tables and illustrations.

This volume, embodying the results of Menshutkin's work on Lomonosov (1711-1765) during the years 1901-1904, contains abridged translations of Latin dissertations copied from manuscripts in the Manuscript Library and in the Archives of the Academy of Sciences, as well as abridged reviews of Lomonosov's Russian memoirs, and covers all of Lomonosov's physicochemical work as known at that time. One chapter is devoted to a description of Lomonosov's chemical laboratory, built in 1748, and contains the first published pictures of its plan and elevation. Lomonosov's lectures on physical chemistry, given at the Academic University, are here published for the first time. The importance of Lomonosov's work is discussed and its bearing upon the history of physics and chemistry.

1905 (2) "M. W. Lomonossow, der erste russische Chemiker und Physiker" (in German). *Annalen der Naturphilosophie*, 4, 204-225.

An abridged account of Lomonosov's life and work in physics and chemistry. First account of his scientific work in a foreign periodical.

1908 (3) "M. V. Lomonosov as a Chemist" (in Russian). *Nature in School Life*, pp. 337-341.

Short popular account for teachers in gymnasia and other middle schools; describes in historical perspective Lomonosov's chemical investigations.

1909 (4) "M. W. Lomonossows Satz der Erhaltung der Energie und des Stoffes" (in German). *Beiträge aus der Geschichte der Chemie*, Leipzig und Wien, pp. 463-467.

Discusses Lomonosov's "general natural law" in relation to the history of the laws of the conservation of matter and of energy. Portrait.

1910 (5) "Physikalisch-chemische Abhandlungen M. W. Lomonossows, 1741-1752" (in German). *Ostwald's Klassiker der exakten Wissenschaften*, No. 178, 60 pages, portrait.

Contains textual excerpts from all of Lomonosov's important physicochemical papers, translated into German by Menshutkin and Max Speter and accompanied by Menshutkin's notes discussing their importance in the history of physics and chemistry.

1911 (6) *M. V. Lomonosov and his Life* (in Russian). St. Petersburg, 160 pages, profusely illustrated.

Popular biography, in which Lomonosov's scientific work—which he always held to be more important than the literary—is given due prominence, as well as his artistic activity (mosaic pictures). Written for the Academy of Sciences on the occasion of the bicentenary of his birth. Eight editions were printed, totaling 75,000 copies.

1911 (7) "M. V. Lomonosov as a Naturalist" (in Russian), 12 pages.

Address, delivered on the occasion of the celebration of the bicentenary of his birth, November 11, 1911, in which he is characterized as a natural philosopher.

1911 (8) "Corpuscular Philosophy of M. V. Lomonosov" (in Russian). *Collection of papers published by the Academy of Sciences*, pp. 151-156.

An account of the natural philosophy of Lomonosov, and of his *magnum opus* which was to contain all of his work on chemistry and physics treated from the atomic point of view. His published dissertations were separate chapters of the projected work.

1911 (9) "M. V. Lomonosov and Phlogiston" (in Russian), *ibid.*, pp. 157-162.

Discussion of Lomonosov's relation to the dominant chemical theories of his time.

1911 (10) "Physicochemical and Geographical Memoirs of Lomonosov" (in Russian). *Physicochemical Papers of the Academy of Sciences*, pp. 1-103.

Russian translations from the Latin of selected papers on physics and chemistry.

1912 (11) "Bicentenary Anniversary of M. V. Lomonosoff's Birthday" (in English). *Chemical News*, 105, 73-75, 85-87 (February 16 and 23, 1912).

Short account of Lomonosov's life and scientific activity, written in answer to an enquiry from Sir William Crookes, editor of *Chemical News*. First account in English based directly on the sources.

1913 (12) "M. V. Lomonosov" (in Russian). *Russian Biographical Dictionary*, 36 pages.

Biography and a complete review, with list, of all of Lomonosov's treatises; bibliography.

1915 (13) "First Russian Scientist" (in Russian). *Knowledge for All*, pp. 1-36.

1923 (14) "Physicochemical Works of Michail Vasilyevich Lomonosov" (in Russian), *Classics of the Natural Sciences*, Moscow, 123 pages with tables and figures.

The chief dissertations and papers of Lomonosov, given partly textually and partly in excerpts in Russian. A short biography and historical introduction are included.

1925 (15) *M. V. Lomonosov* (in Russian), Biographical Library, Moscow, 98 pages with portrait.

Second revised, corrected, and amplified edition of No. 6 above.

1925 (16) "First Russian Chemist" (in Russian). *Century of Chemistry*, No. 1, 4 pages with portrait.

Review of Lomonosov's chemical achievements.

1927 (17) "A Russian Physical Chemist of the Eighteenth Century" (in English). *Journal of Chemical Education*, 4, 1079-1087, with portrait.

General account of the life and physicochemical work of Lomonosov and of its historical significance.

1934 (18) *Collected Works of M. V. Lomonosov*. Published by the Academy of Sciences, Vol. vi, 438 + 131 pages, with many tables and figures. (Edited by Menshutkin with Introduction in Russian.)

Contains the original texts, in Latin or in Russian, of the following listed dissertations: i. Elementa Chymiae Mathematicae; ii. De particulis physicis insensibilibus, corpora naturalia constituentibus, in quibus qualitatum particularium ratio sufficiens continetur; iii. Meditationes de caloris et frigoris causa; iv. De tincturis metallorum; v. Tentamen theoriae de vi aeris elastica; vi. Supplementum ad theoriam de vi aeris elastica; vii. Dissertatio de actione menstruorum chymicorum in genere; viii. Dissertatio de generatione et natura nitri; ix. Dromus ad veram Chymiam Physicam; x. Theoria electricitatis methodo mathematica concinnata; xi. De ratione quantitatis materiae et ponderis; xii. On the frost which occurred after warm weather on April 26, 1755; xiii. Investigation of the cause of aurora borealis; xiv. Anemometrum summan celeritatem cujusvis ventis et simul variationes directionum illius indicans; xv. Consilium de construendo Barometro Universali; xvi. Problema Physica de Tubo nyctoptico; xvii. Nova methodus observandi refractiones radiorum in omni genere pellucidorum corporum; xviii. Conspectus potiorum theorematum, quibus scientiam naturalem locuplectare allaboravit Dn. Michael Lomonosow; xix. Dissertations written as a student at Marburg; xx. Translation into Russian by Lomonosow of Chr. Wolff's *Abridged Experimental Physics*.

1934 (19) *Ibid.*, Vol. VII, 591 pages with many tables and figures. (Edited by Menshutkin with Introduction in Russian.)

Texts of the following: I. De motu aeris in fodinis observato; II. First Fundamentals of Metallurgy; III. Tankar om Isbergens ursprung uti de Nordiska Hafven; IV. Short Description of Different Voyages on Boreal Seas showing the possibility of a passage through the Siberian Ocean to the East Indies; V. Instruction to Sea Commanding Officers going to seek a way to the East on the Boreal Siberian Ocean; VI. Chemical and Optical Notes; VII. Horizontoscope; VIII. Description of a Comet which appeared in the beginning of the year 1744.

1936 (20) *Work of M. V. Lomonosov in Physics and Chemistry* (in Russian). Published by the Academy of Sciences, 537 pages, with numerous tables and figures.

Second edition, entirely recast and rewritten, of No. 1 above. Contains all the new material collected between 1904 and 1936 from a study of Lomonosov's manuscripts in the archives. Consists of sixteen chapters, as follows: I. Preliminary Data; Education Received by Lomonosov; II. Lomonosov as Adjunct and Professor of Chemistry at the Academy of Sciences; III. Atomic and Molecular Theories; IV. On Heat and Cold; V. Kinetic Theory of Air; VI. Electricity; VII. Ether; VIII. Mass and Cohesion; IX. First Chemical Dissertations; X. On Saltpeter; XI. Chemical Laboratory; XII. Laboratory Work; XIII. Physical Chemistry; XIV. Physicochemical Experiments; XV. Metallurgy and Genesis of Metals; XVI. Survey of the Work of Lomonosov as a Physical Chemist. All Latin dissertations are given in textual translations into Russian and Russian memoirs are illustrated by quotations from the originals. Each dissertation is preceded by an historical introduction containing data on the time and circumstances of its composition, of its communication to the academy, etc., and is followed by critical notes showing its relation to the work of predecessors and its bearing on the science of the present.

1936 (21) "M. V. Lomonosov as a Natural Philosopher" (in Russian). *Nature* (Russian), No. 12, pp. 129-137.

A popular account.

1936 (22) "Scientific Work of M. V. Lomonosov" (in Russian). *Messenger of Knowledge*, No. 12, pp. 883-888.

A popular account.

1936 (23) "Lomonosov's Work in Physics and Chemistry" (in Russian). *Pravda*, November 21.

A popular account.

1937 (24) "M. V. Lomonosov's Work in Chemistry and Physics" (in Russian). *Academy of Sciences, Class of Social Sciences*, No. 1, pp. 243-247.

Address given in Moscow on November 21, 1936, at a joint meeting of the Academy of Sciences and the University of Moscow on the occasion of the 225th anniversary of the birth of Lomonosov. General survey of the work of Lomonosov in relation to the science of the present time.

1937 (25) "Life of M. V. Lomonosov" (in Russian). *Bulletin of the Academy of Sciences, Class of Social Sciences,* No. 1, pp. 35-147.

New biography based on contemporary data; full evaluation of Lomonosov's achievements in science, literature, and the arts, and as a statesman and educator.

1937 (26) *Biography of Mikail Vasilyevich Lomonosov* (in Russian). Published by the Academy of Sciences, 238 pages, with many tables and illustrations.

A definitive biography, illustrated profusely.

1937 (27) "Lomonosov" (in Turkish). *Sovieto-Turkish Scientific Collected Papers.*

A popular account translated into Turkish.

INDEX